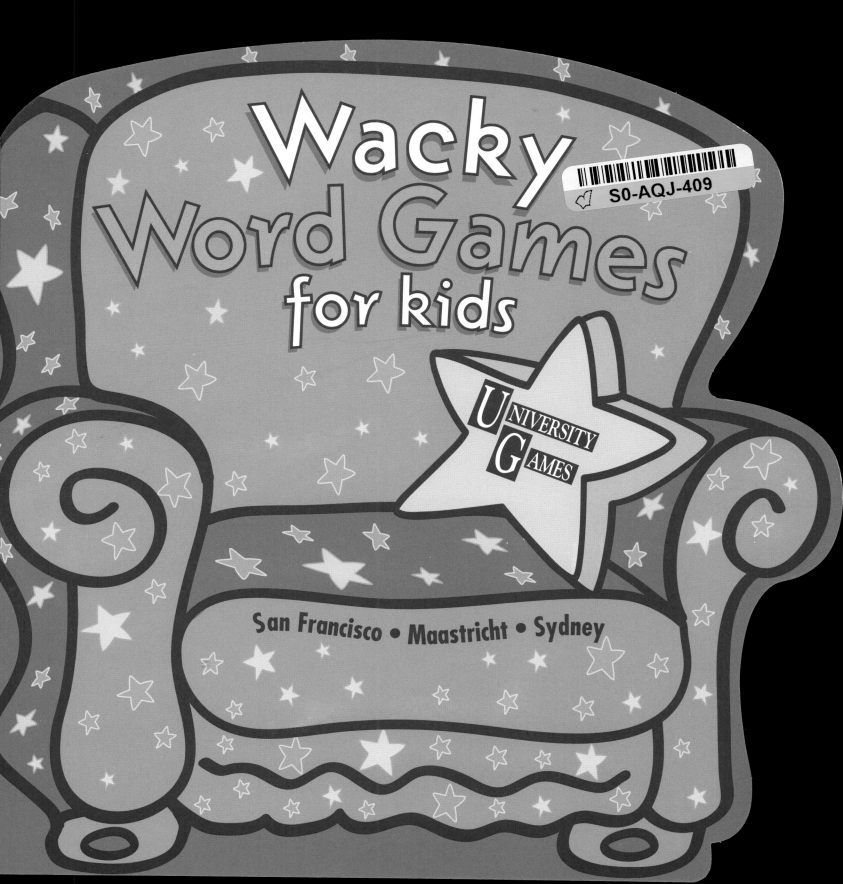

# Wacky Word Games for kids

UNIVERSITY GAMES

San Francisco • Maastricht • Sydney

S0-AQJ-409

## ACKNOWLEDGMENTS

Editorial Director: Erin Conley

Editor: Maria Llull

Cover Design: Amy Aves (of Aves Design)

Interior Design: Laurel Lane

Special thanks to Aidan Anthony, Suzanne Cracraft, Peter Crowell, Elise Gresch, Lynn Gustafson, Michelle Hill, Zack Llull, Jeanette Miller, Bob Moog and Kristen Schoen for their invaluable assistance.

Spinner Books, a division of

University Games Corporation

2030 Harrison Street San Francisco, CA 94110

University Games Europe B.V.

Australielaan 52 6199 AA Maastricht Airport, Netherlands

University Games Australia

10 Apollo Street Warriewood 2102 Australia

Library of Congress Cataloging-in-Publication Data on file with the publisher

ISBN: 1-57528-942-3

Printed in China

1 2 3 4 5 6 7 8 9 10 – 09 08 07 06 05

# Table of Contents

# Introduction

*Wacky Word Games for Kids*™
is filled with enough games and
puzzles to keep you busy for hours
—no matter what kind of mood you're in.

## Feel a little silly?

**Riddles** will fit your mood perfectly.

## Feel like straining your brain?

Turn to the **Brainteasers** section and get
ready to do some serious noodling.

## Feel like putting a puzzle together?

**Word Mud** puzzles are just like jigsaws,
except with letters.

## Feel like a detective?

Check out **30 Second Mysteries** and see
if you can figure out whodunit.

## Feel like finding a needle in a haystack?

**Word Searches** will relieve
that itch lickety-split.

## Feel like dancing?

Well, put down the book and turn on some tunes!

# Riddles

# Animal Antics

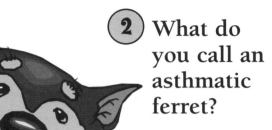

**1** What kind of biscuits should you give to a dog with fleas?

**2** What do you call an asthmatic ferret?

**3** Why did the chicken take a bath?

**5** Why did the poor mother duck cry after counting her ducklings?

**4** What can you do to both a chicken and a guitar?

**6**

**6** What did the parrot say when she wanted a duck for a friend?

*Answers: 1. Biscuits made from scratch. 2. Wheezel (weasel) 3. It smelled fowl. 4. Pluck them. 5. She had too many bills. 6. Polly want a quacker.*

Wacky Word Games · Riddles

# Animal Antics

**7** Why won't the male deer cross the street?

**9** The wolf was wearing sheepskin to blend in with the flock. So why didn't he hunt?

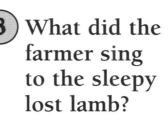

**8** What did the farmer sing to the sleepy lost lamb?

**10** What did one cat say to the cat that missed catching the mouse?

**11** What did the dog trainer shout when the dogs tried to run away?

**12** When is a dog like a mosquito?

7

# Animal Antics

**13** What did the dog say after the kid pulled his book from its teeth?

**14** Why did the big cat get kicked out of the poker game?

**15** What kind of animal could be a butler?

**16** What's a stylish, cool animal?

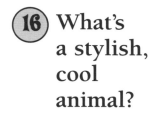

**17** Which bird can lift the most weight?

**18** What animal ought to be oiled?

⭐ 8

# Animal Antics

**19** What animal likes to fib?

**20** Which animal doesn't waste its food?

**22** Why was the alley cat sad?

**21** What did the mother goat say to her son when the rabbit was looking at him?

**23** Why did the bird pour oil on himself?

**24** What is both a bird and a part of eating?

9

Wacky Word Games • Riddles

# Animal Antics

**25** How do you catch a bird that is one-of-a-kind?

**26** How do you catch a wild bird?

**27** How did the boy owl know the girl owl didn't like him?

**28** What did the duck say to the farmer feeding him?

**29** How do you catch a squirrel?

**30** What did the mother elephant say when her girl was misbehaving?

10

Answers: 25. Unique up on it. 26. The tame way. 27. She didn't give a hoot. 28. Put it on my bill. 29. Climb a tree and act like a nut. 30. Tusk tusk

# Animal Antics

**31** What animal is always on the go?

**32** Which animal is a tattle-tale?

**33** What kind of animal can put you to sleep?

**34** What animal can you address fondly?

**36** What did the doe say to the buck about their baby?

**35** Which animal has something in common with Homer Simpson?

11

Answers: 31. A go-rilla 32. The pig—it's a squealer. 33. A boar (bore)
34. A deer (dear) 35. A doe (Doh!) 36. Its fawning all over me.

Wacky Word Games • Riddles

# Animal Antics

**37** What fish will make your piano sound good?

**38** What kind of fish do samurai eat?

**39** What do a lion, a bear, and a train have in common?

**40** What do birds and clocks have in common?

**42** Why did the chicken jump in the mud puddle, cross the road, and then come back again?

**41** What did the old male deer say to the sad young deer?

12

# Animal Antics

**43** Why wouldn't the chicken cross the road?

**45** What do you call a boat full of lambs going to war?

**44** Why didn't the turkey cross the road?

**46** Why wouldn't the cattle laugh at the jokes?

**47** What do you call a polar bear in the desert?

**48** Why should fish know what they weigh?

Answers: 43. He was in a fowl mood. 44. He was too stuffed. 45. A battlesheep 46. They didn't want to be the laughing stock. 47. Lost 48. They have scales.

13

# Animal Antics

**49** What did one reindeer say to the other when he was about to tell a joke?

**50** How many skunks does it take to make a stink?

**51** What did the rattlesnake say to the cobra?

**52** What does a snake take for a headache?

**53** What did the girl boa constrictor say to the boy boa constrictor?

**54** What did the buffalo dad say to his boy when he went out to graze?

★ 14

Answers: 49. This one will sleigh you. 50. A phew 51. You have a great poisonality. 52. Asp-rin 53. I've got a crush on you. 54. Bison (Bye, son)

# Animal Antics

(55) What did the beaver say to the tree?

(56) Why couldn't the dog owner believe that her dog brought back the stick?

(57) What do you get when you cross a pig and a tree?

(58) What do you get when you cross a shark with a snowman?

(59) What do you get when you cross bushes and a pig?

(60) What did the sheriff say when he saw rabbits in his jail?



*Answers: 55. It's been nice gnawing you. 56. Because it was far-fetched. 57. A porcupine 58. Frostbite 59. A hedgehog 60. We're having a bad hare day.*

# Animal Antics

**61** Why has no one ever spotted a leopard in the wild?

**62** What grows down when it grows up?

**63** When does your shoe look like a very hot dog?

**64** What did one skunk say to the other skunk when the hunter came toward them?

**65** Why do sharks swim in salt water?

**66** A parrot that flies away takes what shape?

Answers: 61. *The leopard already has spots.* 62. *A goose* 63. *When its tongue is hanging out.* 64. *Let us spray.* 65. *If they swam in pepper water, they'd sneeze.* 66. *A polygon (polly-gone)*

# Animal Antics

**67** What did the hungry fish say to the fisherman?

**68** What do you get when you cross a bee and a vulture?

**69** Why wouldn't the cowboy ride his girl horse when the sun was out?

**70** What do you get when you cross a golden retriever with a roll?

**71** What do a cat and a coin both have?

**72** What did one skunk say to the other when he missed his target?

17

Answers: 67. Why don't you drop me a line sometime? 68. A buzzard 69. Because she was a nightmare. 70. A dog biscuit 71. A head and a tail 72. You stink at this.

Wacky Word Games • Riddles

# Food for Thought

**1** What did the cucumber say when it saw the small pepper in the fridge?

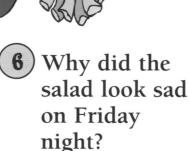
**2** What did one grape say to the other grape at the bottom of the jar?

**3** Why couldn't the basket of corn learn anything?

**18**

**4** What did the boy ear of corn say when he found out the girl ear of corn had a crush on him?

**5** What is the grumpiest fruit?

**6** Why did the salad look sad on Friday night?

Answers: 1. It's a little chill in here. 2. Well, we're in a jam now. 3. Because all the lessons went in one ear and out the other. 4. Aw, shucks. 5. A crab apple 6. Because it was all dressed up with nowhere to go.

Wacky Word Games • Riddles

# Food for Thought

**8** What's a dessert for dads?

**7** Why were the diners disappointed with the nuts?

**9** What kind of tables did the mother want her kid to eat?

**10** What kind of nut has no shell?

**12** What is the nicest fruit?

**11** What's both a dessert and a shoemaker?

19

# Food for Thought

**13** What is the heaviest dessert?

**14** Which dessert could clean the kitchen?

**15** What kind of vegetable nags all the time?

**16** What vegetable keeps growing?

**17** What's the most tired vegetable?

**18** What shouldn't you drink when you have a sore throat?

20

# Food for Thought

**19** Why wouldn't the sugar hang out with the honey?

**20** When is chicken soup not good for you?

**21** What kind of pasta was made today?

**22** How do you make an eggroll?

**23** What are two things you cannot eat for breakfast?

**24** What had the farmer fed the trembling horse?

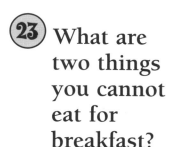

21

# Food for Thought

**25** Why did the baker bake all day and all night?

**26** Why did the tiny baker keep telling jokes when he stood on the bread?

**27** Why did the silly baker put paper wings into a stick of butter?

**22**

**28** Why did the hungry Roman wrestler smile when he ate the lioness?

**29** What did the chewing gum say to the shoe?

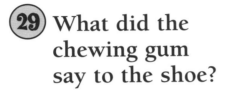

**30** What did the Teddy bear say when the child tried to feed it?

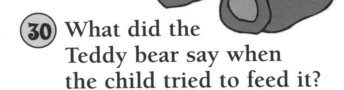

# Food for Thought

**31** What did one candle say to the other candle on the birthday cake?

**32** What's worse than a maggot in the apple you're eating?

**33** What did the refrigerator think when it was unplugged?

**34** Why did the cracker go to bed early?

**35** What did one type of vegetable say to the other when he had to go to the bathroom?

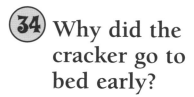

**36** What did Speedy Gonzalez say when someone tried to steal his cheese?

23

# Food for Thought

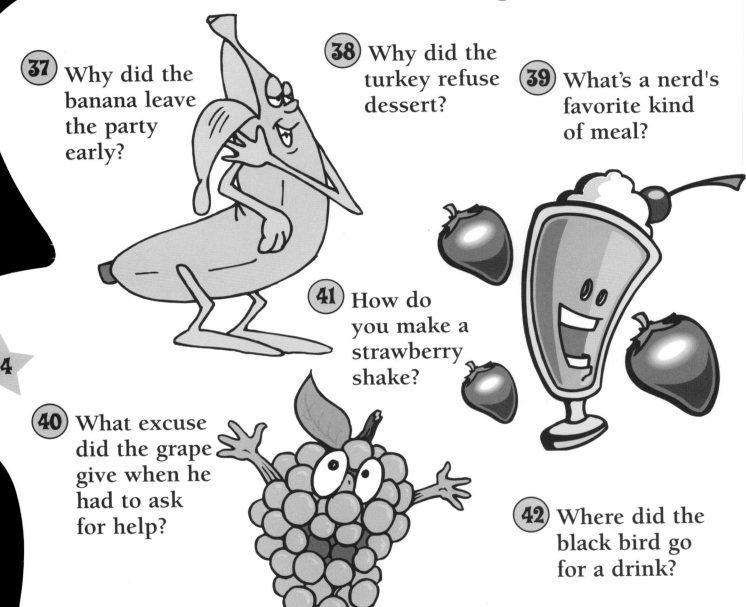

**37** Why did the banana leave the party early?

**38** Why did the turkey refuse dessert?

**39** What's a nerd's favorite kind of meal?

**41** How do you make a strawberry shake?

**40** What excuse did the grape give when he had to ask for help?

**42** Where did the black bird go for a drink?

24

37. Because his friends told him to split.  38. Because he was stuffed.  39. A square meal  40. I'm in a real jam.  41. Shout "BOO!" at it.  42. The crow bar

# Goofy Ghouls

 **2** What did the lady zombie say about the ugly dress?

**1** How did the sandwich disappear from the beach?

**3** What did one ghost say to the other ghost who held a rabbit over its head?

**4** What does a baby ghost drink?

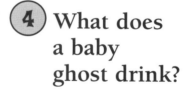

**25**

**5** Why doesn't Dracula have many friends?

**6** Why is it easy to fool Dracula?

Answers: 1. She flew off on her broomstick. 2. I wouldn't be caught dead in that. 3. Now that is hare-raising. 4. Evaporated milk 5. He's a pain in the neck. 6. Because he's such a sucker.

Wacky Word Games · Riddles

# Goofy Ghouls

**7** Why couldn't the mummy see the skeleton in the cave?

**8** Why was the skeleton studying anatomy?

**9** How is a skeleton like an empty house?

★ 26

**10** What did the girl mummy say to the boy mummy?

**11** Why did the ghost put the night on a diet?

**12** Why was the ghost trying to stay away from the cookies?

cookies

tea

Answers: 7. There was no body there. 8. He wanted to bone up on the subject. 9. No body's home.
10. I could get wrapped up in you. 11. He wanted to vanish into thin air. 12. He would go right through them.

# Goofy Ghouls

**13** What did the ghost father say when his son scared the neighbor?

**14** What did one ghoul say to another at the race?

**15** What did the ghoul say to the lifting fog?

**16** Why were the vampires nervous at the monster poker game?

**17** What is the vampire's favorite dance?

**18** What's a monster's favorite drink?

27

# Goofy Ghouls

**20** What did the father goblin say to the giggling goblin boy in the cemetery?

**19** Which monster can never understand directions?

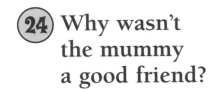

**28**

**21** Why was the ghost sad?

**23** Why didn't the skeleton finish the race?

**22** Which monster has bad table manners?

**24** Why wasn't the mummy a good friend?

*Answers: 19. A where-wolf 20. Stop laughing—this is a grave matter. 21. Because his haunting license expired. 22. The goblin 23. His heart wasn't in it. 24. Because he was too wrapped up in himself.*

## Wacky Word Games · Riddles

# Goofy Ghouls

**25** Why was the girl wizard lost?

**26** Name a holiday that's both friendly and scary.

**27** What position did the phantom play on the soccer team?

**28** What kind of cereal do ghosts eat for breakfast?

**29**

**29** What kind of dog does Dracula have?

**30** What kind of music does a mummy like best?

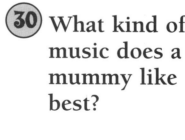

Answers: 25. Because she didn't know witch way to go.  26. Hello-ween  27. Ghoulie
28. Scream of Wheat  29. A bloodhound  30. Wrap (rap)

Wacky Word Games · Riddles

# Goofy Ghouls

**31** What do you call a wizard pilot?

**32** What did the branch say to the little yellow bird on Halloween?

**33** Who did Frankenstein take to the school dance?

**34** What instrument did the skeleton play in the orchestra?

**35** How did the troll get to work?

**36** Why was the school principal so pleased at the Halloween parade?

30

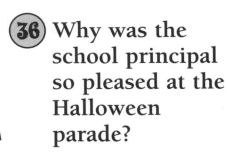

Answers: 31. A flying sorcerer. 32. Twig or tweet! 33. His ghoul friend. 34. The trom-bone 35. He rode the troll-ey. 36. Because there were lots of school spirits.

# Goofy Ghouls

**37** Which New York skyscraper is full of bats?

**38** What kind of cake did the demon serve at his birthday party?

**39** Why did the dragon nap every afternoon?

**40** How did the demon like his eggs?

**31**

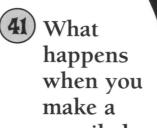

**41** What happens when you make a cannibal mad?

**42** Which side of a black cat has the most fur?

# Freaks of Nature

**1** What happened to the larva that talked and talked?

**2** What kind of bank has fish instead of money?

**3** What has a big mouth but doesn't speak?

**4** What did the beach say to the wave?

**5** What did one leaf say to another leaf when it saw the lumberjack coming?

**6** What did one leaf say to the other leaf when the wind started to blow?

32

Answers: 1. It became a hoarse-fly. 2. A river bank 3. A river 4. You're all washed up. 5. See you in the fall. 6. That's it. I'm leaving.

# Freaks of Nature

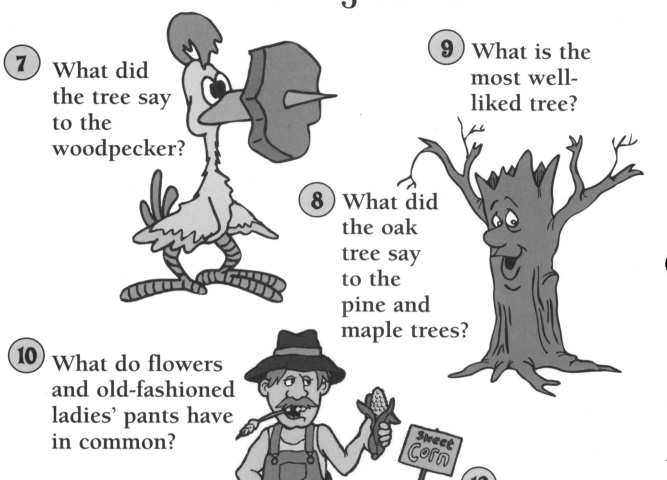

**7** What did the tree say to the woodpecker?

**9** What is the most well-liked tree?

**8** What did the oak tree say to the pine and maple trees?

**10** What do flowers and old-fashioned ladies' pants have in common?

**11** What do flowers and bicycles have in common?

**12** What did the corn say to the whispering farmer?

*Answers: 7. You bore me. 8. You two are so sappy. 9. The poplar tree
10. They are both bloomers. 11. They both have petals/pedals. 12. I can't ear you*

# Freaks of Nature

**13** What did the corn say after the plow crushed it?

**14** What did the boy potato say to the girl potato?

**15** Why was the plant kicked out of the flower shop?

**17** What did the ivy say to the house?

**18** What did the itchy kid yell at the poison ivy?

**16** What happens when a flower has no smell?

34

Answers: 13. That took ears off my life. 14. I only have eyes for you. 15. It wasn't making any scents. 16. Non-scents. 17. You've got me climbing the walls. 18. That was a rash thing to do!

Wacky Word Games • Riddles

# Freaks of Nature

**19** What's both a plant and a well- dressed cat?

**20** What's the weakest plant?

**21** What is the happiest flower?

**22** Which is the laziest mountain?

**23** How do mountains hear?

**24** What did the north wind say to the south wind?

# Freaks of Nature

**25** What promise did the tsunami make to the tiny island?

**26** What did one tsunami say to another?

**27** What is the most impatient storm?

**28** What did the continental plate say after the earthquake?

**30** Why did Zeus puff the clouds away?

**29** What did the boy volcano say to the girl volcano?

⭐ 36

Wacky Word Games • Riddles

# Freaks of Nature

**33** What did the woman say to the bug with sandals on?

**32** What do you call a tiny bug that makes cloth?

**31** Why was the spider so busy?

**36** What kind of ant should you be afraid of?

**34** What kind of bug tells time?

**35** What did the clock say when it saw the two bugs chatting?

**37** ⭐

# Freaks of Nature

**37** What did the drowned bug and the squashed bug have in common?

**38** Which insect is a natural ruler?

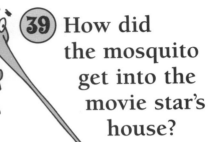

**39** How did the mosquito get into the movie star's house?

**40** What did the hiker say after making it through the first night of his safari?

**41** What did the announcer say at the start of the firefly race?

**42** Why was the compass worried when he couldn't find his way home?

38

# Grab Bag Goodies

**1** What can run but not walk?

**2** Why couldn't the man see through his glasses?

**3** What do you get when you cross a breath mint and a part of your foot?

**4** What do you call the leader of yawners?

**5** What are the best spy shoes?

**6** Why couldn't the rapper fit into his limo?

39

*Answers: 1. Water 2. There was still juice in them. 3. Tic Tac Toe 4. Chairman of the Bored 5. Sneakers 6. Because he was too phat.*

Wacky Word Games • Riddles

# Grab Bag Goodies

**7** What kind of star is not in space?

**8** What do you call a mediocre opera singer?

**9** Why did the two magnets marry?

**40**

**11** Why did the silly girl run through all her neighbors' yards?

**10** Why was the boy at the bottom of the well?

**12** What do you get when the silly knight eats a couple of toy boats?

Answers: 7. A movie star. 8. A so-so prano. 9. Because the attraction was mutual.
10. Because he couldn't leave well enough alone. 11. She wanted to run in the 50-yard dash.
12. Two ships that pass in the knight.

Wacky Word Games • Riddles

# Grab Bag Goodies

**13** What did one math book say to another?

**14** What kind of drum is not a musical instrument?

**15** What's both a musical instrument found in the house and a plate on the baseball field?

**16** What musical instrument will help you catch fish?

**17** How can you tell if a boat is friendly?

**18** Why couldn't the foot feel anything when it stepped on the hot coal?

41

*Answers: 13. You think you've got problems? 14. An ear drum 15. Home bass/base 16. Castanets 17. If it hugs the shore. 18. It was unnerved.*

# Grab Bag Goodies

**19** What did the sock say when the seamstress mended it?

**20** Why did the birthday boy fall over at his surprise party?

**21** What do a groundhog and a lumberjack named Charles have in common?

**23** What day is the brightest day of the week?

**22** Why was the tired kid sleeping next to the chopped-down tree?

**24** What day is perfect for pairs?

Answers: 19. I'm the darndest thing. 20. He was floored. 21. They're both woodchucks. 22. He was sleeping like a log. 23. Sun-day 24. Twos-day

42

# Grab Bag Goodies

**26** What's the best month for soldiers?

**27** What's the best month for polite people?

**25** What's the best day to get married?

**28** What can you break without hurting it?

**29** What has two hands but no arms?

**30** Which people were the greatest wanderers?

43

Answers: 25. Wed-nesday. 26. March. 27. May. 28. A promise. 29. A clock. 30. The Romans

# Grab Bag Goodies

**31** Which people are always hurrying?

**32** What is both a measuring stick and a king?

**33** Which weighs more: a pound of wood or a pound of sand?

**34** What did the silly grandmother give to the kid who asked for a heavy sweater?

**35** Why is Cinderella lousy at basketball?

**36** How can you tell that Robin Hood's arrows were scared?

44

Answers: 31. The Russians 32. A ruler 33. They both weigh the same. 34. A sumo wrestler 35. She is always running away from the ball. 36. They were in a quiver.

# Grab Bag Goodies

**37** What did the dragon hope to find in Hollywood?

**38** Why is everyone tired on April 1st?

**39** Which is faster: hot or cold?

**40** How did the snowman show he was mad?

**41** When is a horseshoe bad luck?

**42** What did one candle ask the other candle?

**45**

# Grab Bag Goodies

**43** Why did the invisible man go crazy?

**44** What did one pair of glasses say to the other pair of glasses?

**45** Why did Humpty Dumpty have a great fall?

**46** What holds up the moon?

**47** What's the difference between a crazy rabbit and counterfeit dollars?

**48** Why did the pirate put the chicken on the ground above his treasure?

46

Wacky Word Games • Riddles

# Grab Bag Goodies

**49** What did the envelope say to the stamp?

**50** What did the boy say when the girl sewed eight buttons on his shirt?

**51** Why doesn't Sweden export its cattle?

**53** What did the soccer ball say to the shoe?

**52** What is in fashion but out of date?

**54** Why are movie stars cool?

★ 47

Answers: 49. Stick with me and we'll go places. 50. You fasten-eight-me. 51. Because it wants to keep its stock-home. (Stockholm) 52. The letter F 53. I get a kick out of you. 54. Because they have so many fans.

# Grab Bag Goodies

**55** Why are cemeteries so full?

**56** How can you make varnish disappear?

**57** If a leprechaun sits on a pot of gold, who sits on silver?

**58** Why was the letter wet?

**59** When is a green book red?

**60** What's the first thing you should do if your sick friend is at the door?

48

# Grab Bag Goodies

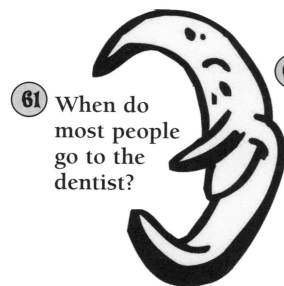

**61** When do most people go to the dentist?

**62** What do the moon and a dollar have in common?

**63** Why is bowling such a quiet sport?

**64** How can you make seven even?

**65** Why does underwear last forever?

**66** What has one horn and gives milk?

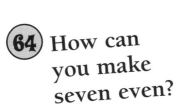

⭐ 49

*Answers: 61. Tooth-hurty 62. They both have four quarters. 63. Because you can hear a pin drop. 64. Take away the S. 65. Because it's never worn out. 66. A milk truck*

**Wacky Word Games • Riddles**

# Grab Bag Goodies

**67** What has eyes but can't see?

**68** What's the hardest thing about learning to roller skate?

**69** Where do you sit at the ballpark if you want to keep your clothes white?

**50**

**72** Why are bells obedient?

**71** What kind of tiles shouldn't you stick to your walls?

**70** What do a driver and a frog have in common?

Wacky Word Games • Riddles

# Grab Bag Goodies

**73** Why did it take so long for King Kong to swallow Big Ben?

**74** What did one keyboard say to the other keyboard?

**75** If April showers bring May flowers, what do May flowers bring?

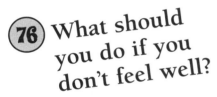

**76** What should you do if you don't feel well?

**77** What's the Easter Bunny's favorite state capital?

**78** What did the father light bulb say to his child?

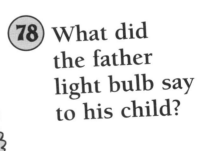

51

Answers: 73. Because it was time-consuming. 74. You're not my type. 75. Pilgrims 76. Take off your mittens. 77. Albunny, NY 78. I wove you watts.

# Grab Bag Goodies

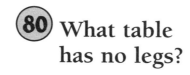

**80** What table has no legs?

**81** Why would the Easter Bunny be good at basketball?

**79** When do you want to catch flies but not hit them?

**52**

**83** How does your bed get longer every night?

**82** The butcher was six feet tall, thin and busy. What did he weigh?

**84** How did the pair of pants feel after being ironed?

Wacky Word Games • Riddles

# Word
# Mud

# Word Mud

Unscramble each word related
to a particular theme.

# It's Not Easy Being Cheesy

izazp ___pizza_____

ilgdelr echese ___grilled_____  ___cheese_____

esehec ecrcaksr ___cheese_____  ___crackers_____

ceehes sfpuf ___cheese_____  ___puffs_____

cnshoa ___nachos_____

isnrgt cehees ___string_____  ___cheese_____

kaeceeeshc ___cheesecake_____

cam dan eecesh ___mac___  ___and___  ___cheese___

creegreuhseb ___cheeseburger_____

zraalzomel ktsisc ___mozzerella_____  ___sticks_____

SOLUTIONS FOUND ON PAGE 90. 55

# Things with Wheels

eskarotbad ___skateboard_____

lleror saedlb ___roller_____ ___blades_____

nahmvii _____ _____

cslooh sbu _____

yecbicl _____

octsreo _____

rcutk _____

srifre wleeh _____ _____

ristgeen elhew _____ _____

lsltroer _____

SOLUTIONS FOUND ON PAGE 90.
56

# Things That Fly

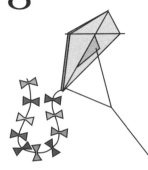

toh ria lnloaob    _____ _____ ____

eirthfg ejt    _____ _____

imagc rctaep    _____ _____

prepa anperial    _____ _____

iekt    _____

plenaic    _____

mipavre tba    _____ ____

lecorethip    _____

ria ocfer eno    ____ ____ ____ ____

ylfgin ruecas    _____ ____

SOLUTIONS FOUND ON PAGE 90.

⭐ 57

# Comic Book Heroes

bmtaan _____

drwoen wmano _____ _____

aaquahm _____

dpiesr amn _____ _____

gimyth uosem _____ _____

aumeshpr _____

evdeadril _____

eergn tennral _____ _____

esiviblni oawmn _____ _____

rldibeneic luhk _____ _____

SOLUTIONS FOUND ON PAGE 90.

# Comic Book Villains

ngiunep

rgene lingob

xle rlohtu

odc okc

ioospn viy

orekj

kpnigni

trnoeiss

omaltle

erddirl

SOLUTIONS FOUND ON PAGE 91.

**59**

# Animal Rhymes

SOLUTIONS FOUND ON PAGE 91.

pceha phsee    _____    _____

ocw ohwc    _____    _____

ribd rned    _____    _____

smihrp ipmbl    _____    _____

xof obx    _____    _____

ianofgml boing    _____    _____

geifafr hlgua    _____    _____

ksunk utrnk    _____    _____

aogt otba    _____    _____

garaknoo rewc    _____    _____

# Animal Talk

og fhis _____ _____

iapbggkcy _____ _____

yppup levo _____ _____

rudgongoh ady _____ _____

bdri aribn _____ _____

aidrblji _____ _____

odg adelpd _____ _____

owikclc _____ _____

kcbal peseh _____ _____

blulrdoez _____ _____

SOLUTIONS FOUND ON PAGE 91.

# A Bad Day at School

mweohkor     ___homework___

dttnieneo     _____

oh secres     ___no___ _____

tets     ___tests_____

terfog hlcnu     _____ _____

smis hte sbu     ____ ____ ____

yast teal     _____ _____

traxe thma     _____ _____

yainr dya     _____ _____

ydtar     _____

SOLUTIONS FOUND ON PAGE 91.

# A Good Day at School

uststbiuet    _____

sresec    _____

efild ript    _____    _____

alhf yad    _____    _____

on krow    _____    _____

on sett    _____    _____

nunsy ayd    _____    _____

tdihbary    _____

tlas dya    _____    _____

aylp sagem    _____    _____

SOLUTIONS FOUND ON PAGE 92.

63

# Lunch Time

ckciehn irnsfeg ——————— ———————

trato stot ——————— ———————

teolamfa ———————————

opus ———————————

iftur eelhater ——————— ———————

ghspeitat ———————————

cashwind ———————————

lgsaana ———————————

rongcsdo ———————————

altsaemlb ———————————

SOLUTIONS FOUND ON PAGE 92.

# Recess Time

edr errov      _____ _____

nemyok sbra      _____ _____

iehd nda eeks      _____ _____ _____

pcohothsc      _____

retllhbeta      _____

jgunmpi eorp      _____ _____

dedog lbal      _____ _____

trapuce het glaf      _____ _____ _____

kalkicbl      _____

kdcu ukcd segoo      _____ _____ _____

SOLUTIONS FOUND ON PAGE 92.

**65**

# US Presidents

olncinl       _____

hsub       _____

enfjrefos       _____

cinnotl       _____

hgaswtnoni       _____

roeotsvle       _____

enarag       _____

traerc       _____

eenndyk       _____

amdas       _____

SOLUTIONS FOUND ON PAGE 93.

# US States

onamnta      _montana_

ohiad      _idaho_

alakas      _alaska_

wngmioy      _wyoming_

earnksba      _nebraska_

ihiaaw      _hawaii_

olaakmho      _oklahoma_

axste      _texas_

sntheeees      _tennessee_

ifrdola      _florida_

SOLUTIONS FOUND ON PAGE 93.

# It's Not Easy Being Blue

rubyreleb

anjse

ubel helaw

eyse

syk

iubbrlde

ixamblo

kioeoc snortem

psiehapr

lebu bornbi

_____

_____

_____  _____

_____

_____

_____

_____

_____  _____

_____

_____  _____

SOLUTIONS FOUND ON PAGE 93.

# It's Not Easy Being Green

anebs          _____

asgrs          _____

imktre         _____

gllatioar      _____

ofgr           _____

veelas         _____

lrcocbio       _____

mesil          _____

tctleve        _____

oscrmkah       _____

SOLUTIONS FOUND ON PAGE 94.

**69**

# Ancient Egypt

nikg utt          _____  _____

enli verri        _____  _____

dirpmya           _____

erlhoyschiigp     _____

coaerlpta         _____

mumym             _____

parahho           _____

rspuayp           _____

iiss              _____

nhpxis            _____

SOLUTIONS FOUND ON PAGE 94.
70

# Dinosaurs

ynshratruuoas exr _____ _____

ousteusrsga _____

caeitsptror _____

uubrsoaelrsat _____

suuraacosbihr _____

rlousetpuasa _____

tnomrmioisuh _____

oearuaslugms _____

sruotngoasugai _____

atrrpivoeloc _____

SOLUTIONS FOUND ON PAGE 94.

**71**

# A Day at the Beach

sveloh _____

lasetc _____

teolw _____

mulblrea _____

srhtsaif _____

snstue _____

ewasede _____

rdfiualeg _____

einseholr _____

kdroalwba _____

SOLUTIONS FOUND ON PAGE 95.

**72**

# A Day at the Zoo

riglola _____

inlo _____

riteg _____

anheeplt _____

rabez _____

kroanoga _____

reaigff _____

npgneiu _____

telaneop _____

omagilfn _____

SOLUTIONS FOUND ON PAGE 95.

**73**

# Famous Bears

neeianbstr rseab   _____    _____

gioy ebra   _____    _____

newini het opho   _____    _____    \_\_\_\_

emkoys eht erba   _____    _____    \_\_\_\_

zfoezi   _____

oloab   _____

umgym asrbe   _____    _____

dryroocu   _____

eth erteh arebs   _____    _____    \_\_\_\_

anitnogpdd   _____

SOLUTIONS FOUND ON PAGE 95.

74

# Famous Monkeys

uivocrs egorge    _____    _____

bnooz    _____

ingk gokn    _____    _____

sbebulb    _____

bau    _____

ookk    _____

scok menkyo    _____    _____

ikrfai    _____

ydoken nokg    _____    _____

rm linssno    _____    _____

SOLUTIONS FOUND ON PAGE 96.

75

# Happy Campers

erfmaicp     _____

lssaawmhorlm     _____

kkcabcap     _____

hgfihsllat     _____

seomrs     _____

nrlnate     _____

ghifnsi elop     _____    _____

itotle eprap     _____    _____

rltia ixm     _____    _____

pocsmas     _____

SOLUTIONS FOUND ON PAGE 96.

# Creeps

eafl _____

aooptt gbu _____ - _____

rpised _____

inptedece _____

reasmaalnd _____

knase _____

kcgeo _____

icsronpo _____

rnigyap iantsm _____ - _____

linsa _____

SOLUTIONS FOUND ON PAGE 96.

77

# Shiver Me Timbers

sullk       _____

veretras pma      _____    _____

obcosessnr      _____

lbcak lfga      _____    _____

raotrp      _____

iartep      _____

lkwa het kpanl    _____   _____   _____

vsruyc      _____

ibrdue rresutea    _____    _____

lyljo gerro      _____    _____

SOLUTIONS FOUND ON PAGE 97.

# Storming the Castle

hnitkg      _____

otam      _____

egnundo      _____

gink dna euqne      _____ _____ _____

osjtu      _____

nngiihs morra      _____ _____

chael      _____

qesiru      _____

lhvrcyia      _____

belon tesed      _____ _____

SOLUTIONS FOUND ON PAGE 97.

**79**

# Trick or Treat

dacyn rnco      _____    _____

npimukp cvigrna   _____    _____

onffci       _____

mstueoc       _____

auadcrl       _____

tgohss        _____

swcheti       _____

flul omon      _____    _____

crbetoo       _____

octhcelao srba    _____    _____

SOLUTIONS FOUND ON PAGE 97.

# Fantasy World

citmeoanr     _____

gadonr     _____

fdraw     _____

imdream     _____

iyrfa     _____

neomg     _____

lnogib     _____

tlrlo     _____

niuncro     _____

cruaten     _____

SOLUTIONS FOUND ON PAGE 98.

81

# Deep Sea Diving

SOLUTIONS FOUND ON PAGE 98.

ootscup _____

tcehocnala _____

agter thewi krash _____ _____ _____

tyasngri _____

rardcuaab _____

lerectci lee _____ _____

iflcesttuh _____

sehserao _____

ohorehses bcra _____ _____

mpahkbuc lehwa _____ _____

# Lost in Space

omno skorc

————————————— —————————————

rdasteio

————————————— —————————————

mocte

———————————————————————————

kymil ywa

————————————— —————————————

gbi þeiþdr

————————————— —————————————

epasc seuhltt

————————————— —————————————

scepa otisant

————————————— —————————————

rmsa vrero

————————————— —————————————

ohtatuars

———————————————————————————

heveynla ebsiod

————————————— —————————————

SOLUTIONS FOUND ON PAGE 98.

83

# Stormy Weather

nighlitgn     _____

duhntre     _____

ailh     _____

ianr     _____

tseel     _____

wson     _____

otdorna     _____

ihecnrrua     _____

ntooyph     _____

crlopait mtsor     _____    _____

SOLUTIONS FOUND ON PAGE 99.

84

# "C" Food

arcosrt _____

earlce _____

radceem oncr _____ _____

eaauocnltp _____

ekoioc _____

udrstac _____

ecka _____

ecsresola _____

roatnssic _____

rclfiwluoae _____

SOLUTIONS FOUND ON PAGE 99.

85

# It's Not Easy Being Red

pots sngi     _____   _____

kcbri     _____

feri tcruk     _____   _____

rcdianla     _____

etrslob     _____

byadglu     _____

arsm     _____

totaom     _____

oeml     _____

nowlc eson     _____   _____

SOLUTIONS FOUND ON PAGE 99.

# It's Not Easy Being Yellow

shnnieus          _____

addfflio          _____

emonl             _____

gbi dibr          _____  _____

axit              _____

anaryc            _____

anbnaa            _____

orcn no eht bco   ____  ____  ____  ____  ____

shuqas            _____

cdku              _____

SOLUTIONS FOUND ON PAGE 100.

87

# Book Characters

ryrha otpert

_____ _____

erelchruykb nifn

_____ _____

nena aknfr

_____ _____

pipip gnctoiknogls

_____ _____

idelerbuaa rposnha

_____ _____

hte hncgri

_____ _____

deenlaim

_____

lbobi agbsngi

_____ _____

arlehci ketbuc

_____ _____

fgor dan oadt

____ _____ ____

SOLUTIONS FOUND ON PAGE 100.

# Color Rhymes

kithn nkpi _____ _____

amngo gaton _____ _____

nowrb wconr _____ _____

elmowl ylwole _____ _____

ubel tooatt _____ _____

eatl lehwe _____ _____

wteih tgkinh _____ _____

ckbal skhca _____ _____

edr ebd _____ _____

reneg ncaehmi _____ _____

SOLUTIONS FOUND ON PAGE 100.

89

# Solutions

**P. 55**

## It's Not Easy Being Cheesy

izazp = pizza
ilgdelr echese = grilled cheese
esehec ecrcaksr = cheese crackers
ceehes sfpuf = cheese puffs
cnshoa = nachos
isnrgt cehees = string cheese
kaeceeeshc = cheesecake
cam dan eecesh = mac and cheese
creegreuhseb = cheeseburger
zraalzomel ktsisc = mozzarella sticks

**P. 56**

## Things with Wheels

eskarotbad = skateboard
lleror saedlb = roller blades
nanmvii = minivan
cslooh sbu = school bus
yecbicl = bicycle
octsreo = scooter
rcutk = truck
srifre wleeh = Ferris wheel
ristgeen elhew = steering wheel
lsltroer = stroller

**P. 57**

## Things that Fly

toh ria lnloaob = hot air balloon
eirthfg ejt = fighter jet
imagc rctaep = magic carpet
prepa anperial = paper airplane
iekt = kite
plenaic = pelican
mipavre tba = vampire bat
lecorethip = helicopter
ria ocfer eno = Air Force One
ylfgin ruecas = flying saucer

**P. 58**

## Comic Book Heroes

bmtaan = Batman
drwoen wmano = Wonder Woman
aaquanm = Aquaman
dpiesr amn = Spider Man
gimyth uosem = Mighty Mouse
aumesnpr = Superman
evdeadril = Daredevil
eergn tennral = Green Lantern
esiviblni oawmn = Invisible Woman
rldibeneic luhk = Incredible Hulk

# Solutions

## P. 59
### Comic Book Villains

ngiunep = Penguin
rgene lingob = Green Goblin
xle rlohtu = Lex Luthor
odc ock = Doc Ock
ioospn viy = Poison Ivy
orekj = Joker
kpnigni = Kingpin
trnoeiss = Sinestro
omaltle = Metallo
erddirl = Riddler

## P. 60
### Animal Rhymes

pceha phsee = cheap sheep
ocw ohwc = cow chow
ribd rned = bird nerd
smihrp ipmbl = shrimp blimp
xof obx = fox box
ianofgml boing = flamingo bingo
geifafr hlgua = giraffe laugh
ksunk utrnk = skunk trunk
aogt otba = goat boat
garaknoo rewc = kangaroo crew

91

## P. 61
### Animal Talk

og fhis = go fish
iapbggkcy = piggyback
yppup levo = puppy love
rudgongoh ady = groundhog day
bdri aribn = bird brain
aidrblji = jailbird
odg adelpd = dog paddle
owikclc = cowlick
kcbal peseh = black sheep
blulrdoez = bulldozer

## P. 62
### A Bad Day at School

mweohkor = homework
dttnieneo = detention
on secres = no recess
tets = test
terfog hlcnu = forget lunch
smis hte sbu = miss the bus
yast teal = stay late
traxe thma = extra math
yainr dya = rainy day
ydtar = tardy

# Solutions

**P. 63**

## A Good Day at School

uststbiuet = substitute
sresec = recess
efild ript = field trip
alhf yad = half day
on krow = no work
on sett = no test
nunsy ayd = sunny day
tdihbary = birthday
tlas dya = last day
aylp sagem = play games

**P. 64**

## Lunch Time

ckciehn irnsfeg = chicken fingers
trato stot = tator tots
teolamfa = meatloaf
opus = soup
iftur eelhater = fruit leather
ghspeitat = spaghetti
cashwind = sandwich
lgsaana = lasagna
rongcsdo = corndogs
altsaemlb = meatballs

**P. 65**

## Recess Time

edr errov =  red rover
nemyok sbra =  monkey bars
iehd nda eeks =  hide and seek
pcohothsc =  hopscotch
retllhbeta =  tetherball
jgunmpi eorp =  jumping rope
dedog lbal =  dodge ball
trapuce het glaf  =  capture the flag
kalkicbl =  kickball
kdcu ukcd segoo =  duck duck goose

92

# Solutions

## P. 66

### US Presidents

olncinl = Lincoln
hsub = Bush
enfjrefos = Jefferson
cinnotl = Clinton
hgaswtnoni = Washington
roeotsvle = Roosevelt
enarag = Reagan
traerc = Carter
eenndyk = Kennedy
amdas = Adams

## P. 67

### US States

onamnta = Montana
ohiad = Idaho
alakas = Alaska
wngmioy = Wyoming
earnksba = Nebraska
ihiaaw = Hawaii
olaakmho = Oklahoma
axste = Texas
sntneeees = Tennessee
ifrdola = Florida

## P. 68

### It's Not Easy Being Blue

rubyreleb = blueberry
anjse = jeans
ubel helaw = blue whale
eyse = eyes
syk = sky
iubbrlde = bluebird
ixamblo = mailbox
kioeoc snortem = Cookie Monster
psiehapr = sapphire
lebu bornbi = blue ribbon

# Solutions

## P. 69

### t's Not Easy Being Green

anebs = beans
asgrs = grass
imktre = Kermit
gllatioar = alligator
ofgr = frog
veelas = leaves
lrcocbio = broccoli
mesil = slime
tctleue = lettuce
oscrmkah = shamrock

## P. 70

### Ancient Egypt

nikg utt = King Tut
enli verri = Nile River
dirpmya = pyramid
erlhoyschiigp = hieroglyphics
coaerlpta = Cleopatra
mumym = mummy
parahho = pharaoh
rspuayp = papyrus
iiss = Isis
nhpxis = sphinx

## P. 71

### Dinosaurs

ynsnratruuoas exr = *Tyrannosaurus rex*
ousteusrsga = *Stegosaurus*
caeitsptror = *Triceratops*
uubrsoaelrsat = *Albertosaurus*
suuraacosbihr = *Brachiosaurus*
rlousetpuasa = *Plateosaurus*
tnomrmioisuh = *Ornithomimus*
oearuaslugms = *Megalosaurus*
sruotngoasugai = *Giganotosaurus*
atrrpivoeloc = *Velociraptor*

94

# Solutions

## P. 72

### A Day at the Beach

sveloh = shovel
lasetc = castle
teolw = towel
mulblrea = umbrella
srhtsaif = starfish
snstue = sunset
ewasede = seaweed
rdfiualeg = lifeguard
einseholr = shoreline
kdroalwba = boardwalk

## P. 73

### A Day at the Zoo

riglola = gorilla
inlo = lion
riteg = tiger
anheeplt = elephant
rabez = zebra
kroanoga = kangaroo
reaigff = giraffe
npgneiu = penguin
telaneop = antelope
omagilfn = flamingo

## P. 74

### Famous Bears

neeianbstr rseab = Berenstain Bears
gioy ebra = Yogi Bear
newini het opho = Winnie the Pooh
emkoys eht erba = Smokey the Bear
zfoezi = Fozzie
oloab = Baloo
umgym asrbe = Gummy Bears
dryroocu = Corduroy
eth erteh arebs = The Three Bears
anitnogpdd = Paddington

95

# Solutions

## P. 75

### Famous Monkeys

uiuocrs egorge = Curious George
bnooz = Bonzo
ingk gokn = King Kong
sbebulb = Bubbles
bau = Abu
ookk = Koko
scok menkyo = Sock Monkey
ikrfai = Rafiki
ydoken nokg = Donkey Kong
rm linssno = Mr Nilsson

## P. 76

### Happy Campers

erfmaicp = campfire
lssaawmhorlm = marshmallows
kkcabcap = backpack
hgfihsllat = flashlight
seomrs = smores
nrlnate = lantern
ghifnsi elop = fishing pole
itotle eprap = toilet paper
rltia ixm = trail mix
pocsmas = compass

## P. 77

### Creeps

eafl = flea
aooptt gbu = potato bug
rpised = spider
inptedece = centipede
reasmaalnd = salamander
knase = snake
kcgeo = gecko
icsronpo = scorpion
rnigyap iantsm = praying mantis
linsa = snail

# Solutions

## P. 78

### Shiver Me Timbers

sullk = skull

ueretras pma = treasure map

obcosessnr = crossbones

lbcak lfga = black flag

raotrp = parrot

iartep = pirate

lkwa het kpanl = walk the plank

vsruyc = scurvy

ibrdue rresutea = buried treasure

lyljo gerro = Jolly Roger

## P. 79

### Storming the Castle

hnitkg = knight

otam = moat

egnundo = dungeon

gink dna euqne = king and queen

osjtu = joust

nngiihs morra = shining armor

cnael = lance

qesiru = squire

lhvrcyia = chivalry

belon tesed = noble steed

## P. 80

### Trick or Treat

dacyn rnco = candy corn

npimukp cvigrna = pumpkin carving

onffci = coffin

mstueoc = costume

auadcrl = Dracula

tgohss = ghosts

swcheti = witches

flul omon = full moon

crbetoo = October

octhcelao srba = chocolate bars

# Solutions

## P. 81

### Fantasy World

citmeoanr = manticore
gadonr = dragon
fdraw = dwarf
imdream = mermaid
iyrfa = fairy
neomg = gnome
lnogib = goblin
tlrlo = troll
niuncro = unicorn
cruaten = centaur

## P. 82

### Deep Sea Diving

ootscup = octopus
tcehocnala = coelacanth
agter thewi krash = great white shark
tyasngri = stingray
rardcuaab = barracuda
lerectci lee = electric eel
iflcesttuh = cuttlefish
sehserao = seahorse
ohorehses bcra = horseshoe crab
mpahkbuc lehwa = humpback whale

## P. 83

### Lost in Space

omno skorc = moon rocks
rdasteio = asteroid
mocte = comet
kymil ywa = Milky Way
gbi peipdr = Big Dipper
epasc seuhltt = Space Shuttle
scepa otisant = space station
rmsa vrero = Mars Rover
ontatuars = astronaut
heveynla ebsiod = heavenly bodies

98

# Solutions

## P. 84

### Stormy Weather

nighlitgn = lightning
duhntre = thunder
ailh = hail
ianr = rain
tseel = sleet
wson = snow
otdorna = tornado
ihecnrrua = hurricane
ntooyph = typhoon
crlopait mtsor = tropical storm

## P. 85

### "C" Food

arcosrt = carrots
earlce = cereal
radceem oncr = creamed corn
eaauocnltp = cantaloupe
ekoioc = cookie
udrstac = custard
ecka = cake
ecsresola = casserole
roatnssic = croissant
rclfiwluoae = cauliflower

## P. 86

### It's Not Easy Being Red

pots sngi =  stop sign
kcbri =  brick
feri tcruk =  fire truck
rcdianla =  cardinal
etrslob =  lobster
byadglu =  ladybug
arsm =  Mars
totaom =  tomato
oeml =  Elmo
nowlc eson =  clown nose

# Solutions

**P. 87**

## It's Not Easy Being Yellow

shnnieus = sunshine
addfflio = daffodil
emonl = lemon
gbi dibr = Big Bird
axit = taxi
anaryc = canary
anbnaa = banana
orcn no eht bco = corn on the cob
shuqas = squash
cdku = duck

**P. 88**

## Book Characters

ryrha otpert = Harry Potter
erelchruykb nifn = Huckleberry Finn
nena aknfr = Anne Frank
pipip gnctoiknogls = Pippi Longstocking
idelerbuaa rposnha = Baudelaire orphans
hte hncgri = The Grinch
deenlaim = Madeline
lbobi agbsngi = Bilbo Baggins
arlehci ketbuc = Charlie Bucket
fgor dan oadt = Frog and Toad

100

**P. 89**

## Color Rhymes

kithn nkpi = think pink
amngo gaton = mango tango
nowrb wconr = brown crown
elmowl ylwole = mellow yellow
ubel tooatt = blue tattoo
eatl lehwe= teal wheel
wteih tgkinh = white knight
ckbal skhca = black shack
edr ebd = red bed
reneg ncaehmi = green machine

# Brainteasers

# The circle game

Geometry is hard for Silly Sally.

Which is **BIGGER?**  a square with a 1 foot side

or

a circle with a 1 foot diameter?

SOLUTIONS FOUND ON PAGE 127.

**102**

## Paw Paw's Handyman

Quincy can paint a room in 6 hours.

Emmitt can paint the same room in 3 hours.

**How long will it take if they are both painting?**

Wacky Word Games • Brainteasers

# The Disappearing Pickles

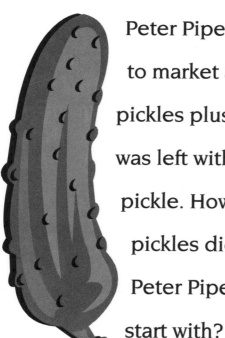

Peter Piper the pickle salesman went to market and sold half of his pickles plus half a pickle. He was left with one whole pickle. How many pickles did Peter Piper start with?

## Pied Piper Wanted

How many rats are in the room if there is a rat in each of the 4 corners and 3 rats across from every rat and a rat in the corner next to every rat?

SOLUTIONS FOUND ON PAGE 127.

103

Wacky Word Games • Brainteasers

# Lost in Space

In what state would you find yourself if you

left St. Louis and went five miles east, then

200 miles north and then

40 miles west?

**5 mi E ▷**

**200 mi N △**

**40 mi W ◁**

SOLUTIONS FOUND ON PAGE 127.

**104**

# over easy

**Who am I?**

I am a very fragile, rotund little man. I once had an accident that left me so disfigured that even the King of England and his fine staff failed at attempts to repair me.

# Most  Wanted ?

**In which state capitals will you find these guys?**

Al

Jeff

Sal

Harris

## Winter Construction

Lani's hands were freezing after building a snowman without any gloves. Should Lani warm up by putting her hands under cold water or hot water?

SOLUTIONS FOUND ON PAGE 128.

Wacky Word Games · Brainteasers

# Light Show

What is the name of the toy constructed by placing multiple mirrors at different angles and shooting light through a tube, bouncing the light from one mirror to the next?

SOLUTIONS FOUND ON PAGE 128.

# Dog Dayz

What is the next letter in this series?

## D N O S A J

# Just Kidding

"Let's go play with the 3 kids up on that hill," said Silly Sally. Joe ran ahead but only found 2 children and some grazing farm animals when he arrived. Where did the third kid go?

# Buried Treasure

SOLUTIONS FOUND ON PAGE 128.

**107**

Is it against the law to bury a person in Utah who is permanently living in Nevada?

Wacky Word Games · Brainteasers

# Go West, Young Girl

N

**Erin left New York and flew to California. The flight took five hours. If Erin left at 11:00 am, when did she arrive?**

W - - - - - - - E

S

SOLUTIONS FOUND ON PAGE 129.

**108**

## I am C·O·U·N·T·I·N·G on you

**What number is ONE**

**more than TEN HUNDRED and one?**

## All in the Family

Try to name the three most closely related pairs of presidents.

## Wait Until Dark

Jacob and Lutz were camping in June. Before going to sleep they decided to read a book. They both agreed to stop reading when it got dark. They were not fast readers, but they both finished the entire encyclopedia. How?

SOLUTIONS FOUND ON PAGE 129.

109

Wacky Word Games • Brainteasers

# Sister Sprinters

Nina and Lydia start from their home and each run 2 miles. Nina can run a mile in 8 minutes 30 seconds and Lydia can run a mile in 9 minutes 10 seconds. When they finish running, what is the farthest apart they can be?

SOLUTIONS FOUND ON PAGE 129.

**110**

**Sunrise, Sunset**

can't be found at noon

What starts today,

and is required to end sunset?

# Digestive Detective

Jeff and Vinnie met for dinner at Fitz's Fine Foods. After they both went to the bathroom they sat down and ordered. The waiter described the special as trout almondine with asparagus covered in hollandaise sauce. Jeff said, "I'll take it, but Vinnie wants something else. He had asparagus for lunch."

How did Jeff know what Vinnie had for lunch?

# 3 Men and a Lady

SOLUTIONS FOUND ON PAGE 130.

**111**

Melissa went to dinner with
Andrew,
George
and
Ulysses,
but she ate **alone**.

Not surprisingly, they all showed up to pay for her meal. **Why?**

Wacky Word Games • Brainteasers

# Can YOU canoe?

TWO fathers and TWO sons went on a canoe trip,

## ONE fell out

and TWO were left.

Where is the 4th man?

SOLUTIONS FOUND ON PAGE 130.

## Hi Ho Silver

Ben Cartwright rode into Virginia City late on Friday. Ben Cartwright stayed two days, but still rode out on Friday.

Explain.

Wacky Word Games • Brainteasers

# Talking States

What did Flora-di of?

What did Tenna see?

What did Della wear?

## Sheila the GREAT

SOLUTIONS FOUND ON PAGE 130.

113

Sheila lives in Chicago. One night she sat down for dinner with the window open and heard a gunshot. Then she witnessed two gruesome deaths. Before she could leave the room she saw a building catch fire. Why didn't Sheila call the police?

Wacky Word Games • Brainteasers

# Down Under

Shane bet Steve that it was impossible to go back in time.

Why did Shane agree that Steve won the bet when their plane arrived in Los Angeles, California from Adelaide, Australia?

SOLUTIONS FOUND ON PAGE 131.

114

# Double Trouble

Pacific Ocean

Atlantic Ocean

In what US city can you visit a state capital, see the Atlantic Ocean, drive an hour to the Pacific Ocean and see 17th-century architecture?

# Birthday Boy

**Horace Jordan was born in February 1896. Why did he only celebrate his first birthday in 1904?**

Road Trip

SOLUTIONS FOUND ON PAGE 131.

115

Which state capitals would you visit to find a...

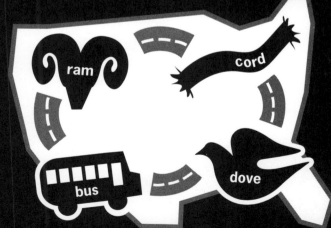

ram

cord

bus

dove

Wacky Word Games · Brainteasers

# Happy Family

Homer's mother has four children.

Three of them are named
Spring,
Summer
and
Autumn.

What is the
fourth named?

SOLUTIONS FOUND ON PAGE 131.

116

# Campfire

Jeff Glik
is camping
outside Bemidji,
Minnesota with only
oil lamps, a candle
and some birch
bark. He has only one
match. Which should
he light first?

# BUS STOP

**125**

If 50 kids fit in a school bus, how many buses do you need to get 125 kids to school?

## Time to Go

Mr. Rosner walked into the room and noticed Silly Sally sitting patiently on the floor reading a magazine. Mr. Rosner's alarm clock was totally destroyed and parts were all over the room. What had Silly Sally been up to?

SOLUTIONS FOUND ON PAGE 132.

117

Wacky Word Games · Brainteasers

# Wide Load

Mr. Stone's truck attempted to enter a parking garage, but got caught underneath the garage ceiling because of the truck's 6'6" height. It won't budge forward or backward. How can he get the truck out from under the garage ceiling?

SOLUTIONS FOUND ON PAGE 132.

**118**

## Compass Confusion

N

One summer morning Emily decided to drive from her favorite casino in Reno, NV to visit her mom in Los Angeles, CA. Did Emily travel east or west?

S

W

E

Wacky Word Games · Brainteasers

# Phone Tree

**Maia wants to call all 10 kids in her 6th grade class**

and then have each of them talk to each of the others.

What is the minimum number of conversations that will take place?

SOLUTIONS FOUND ON PAGE 132.

119

## Traveling Abroad

**Name the European cities where Silly Sally went to find the following boys:**

**Don**

**Lin**

**Bud**

**Ari**

(Hint: She went to Toronto to find Ron.)

Wacky Word Games · Brainteasers

# Chirp Chirp

**What do the following birds have in common?**

cardinals  ravens  eagles  falcons

SOLUTIONS FOUND ON PAGE 133.

120

# If I Ran the ZOO

In what northern hemisphere city can you find indigenous tigers and lions?

Wacky Word Games • Brainteasers

# Life's Lessons

What is it that you *need* to have life,

you won't have with death

and you can't start fun without?

## The Getaway

SOLUTIONS FOUND ON PAGE 133.

**121**

Matt Brooks often goes
the wrong way on a
one-way street— PAST
a police station.
How does he get away
with it without ever
breaking the law?

# Riddle Me This

I sizzle like bacon.
I'm made with an egg.
I've got lots of backbone,
but not even one leg.
I peel like an onion,
yet still remain whole.
I'm long like a fishpole,
but fit in a hole.

**What am I?**

SOLUTIONS FOUND ON PAGE 133.

122

# Exciting

Hey, genius!

I start with the letter E.
I end with the letter E.
I usually contain one letter.
But I am not the letter E.

What am I?

# I'm Never Blue

Sometimes I'm green,
sometimes I'm black.
When I'm yellow,
I'm a very nice fellow.
That's when I'm feeling
mighty a-peeling.

What am I?

## Who Was That Masked Man?

SOLUTIONS FOUND ON PAGE 134.

123

Elizabeth has been working hard and she wants to go home. The masked man won't let her.

Why?

Wacky Word Games · Brainteasers

# Out of Touch

Hey, what's up?
They don't touch when you say "TOUCH"
—but they *do* touch when you say "SEPARATE."

**What are they?**

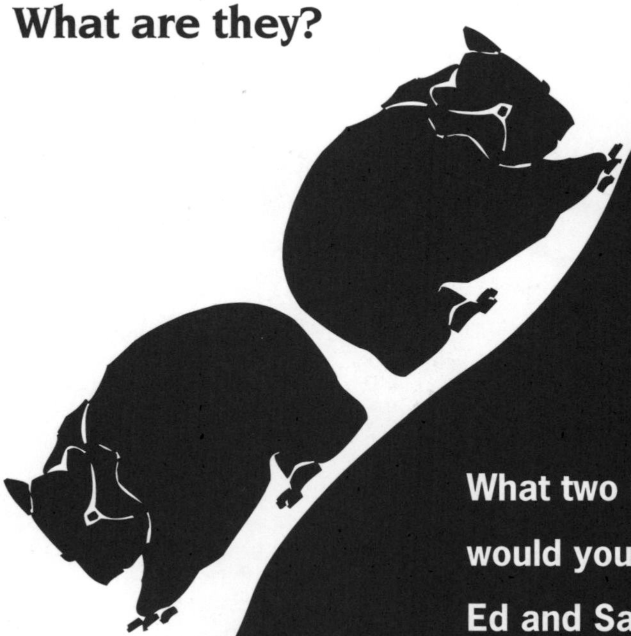

SOLUTIONS FOUND ON PAGE 134.

124

# E·X·T·R·A Credit

What two European cities
would you visit to find
Ed and Sara?

Sara

Ed

Wacky Word Games · Brainteasers

# Freezer Burn

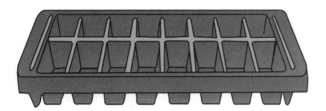

What did Chris the Confused
pull out of the freezer
and proudly offer to
his hungry father
for dessert?

## SSSSSSS

SOLUTIONS FOUND ON PAGE 134.

125

What word becomes plural
when an "s" is added,
but becomes singular again
by adding another "s"?

# Fur Sure

Scientists have found that
cats are furrier on one side than
the other. The side with the most
fur is the side that cats most often lie
on. Which side of a cat has more fur?

SOLUTIONS FOUND ON PAGE 134.

# Roll Out
# the Barrel

Rick Tuttle is asked to carry a

barrel of water across the desert

for his Cub Scout troop.

The barrel is 2 feet high,

1.5 feet in diameter and

it weighs 100 pounds.

What can he add to it

to make it lighter?

# Solutions

**Page 102**
**The Circle Game**
A square has a larger area, since the circle with a 1-foot diameter will actually fit inside a square with a 1-foot side.

**Page 102**
**Paw-Paw's Handyman**
2 hours (Emmitt can paint 1/3 of the room in an hour while Quincy can paint 1/6 of the room in an hour. In 2 hours they will paint 2/3 + 2/6 = 1 entire painted room.)

**Page 103**
**The Disappearing Pickle**
Three. If he sold half of his pickles, that would leave him with one and a half. Then selling a half, he has one pickle left.

**Page 103**
**Pied Piper Wanted**
4 rats: There are only 4 corners to the room.

**Page 104**
**Lost in Space**
State of confusion! More likely close to Burlington, Iowa.

**Page 104**
**Over Easy**
Humpty Dumpty

127

# Solutions

**Page 105**
**Most Wanted**
Jeff      (Jefferson City, MO)
Harris    (Harrisburg, PA)
Sal       (Salem, OR)
Al        (Albany, NY)

**Page 105**
**Winter Construction**
Cold water (She wouldn't feel how hot the hot water was and could burn herself badly.)

**Page 106**
**Light Show**
A kaleidoscope

**Page 106**
**Dog Dayz**
J (June—the letters are the first letters of the months of the year in reverse order.)

**Page 107**
**Just Kidding**
The third kid was a baby goat.

**Page 107**
**Buried Treasure**
Yes (It is illegal to bury a living person.)

128

# Solutions

**Page 108**
**Go West, Young Girl**
1:00 pm (There is a three-hour time difference.)

**Page 108**
**I am Counting on You**
One thousand (ten hundred) and two, 1002.

**Page 109**
**All in the Family**
John Adams (father)–
John Quincy Adams (son)
George H. Bush (father)–
George W. Bush (son)
William H. Harrison
    (grandfather)–
Benjamin Harrison
    (grandson)

**Page 109**
**Wait Until Dark**
They were in Lapland, land of the midnight sun, and the sun didn't set until September.

129

**Page 110**
**Sister Sprinters**
Four miles (They ran in opposite directions.)

**Page 110**
**Sunrise, Sunset**
The letter "t"

# Solutions

**Page 111**
**Digestive Detective**
When they went to the bathroom, Jeff noticed that Vinnie's urine was green (and smelly too!). Jeff's deductive reasoning told him that the source of the color was a recent experience with asparagus.

**Page 111**
**3 Men and a Lady**
Mr. George Washington, Mr. Andrew Jackson and Mr. Ulysses S. Grant are paper money. Her meal cost $71 with gratuity. Washington is on the $1 bill, Jackson is pictured on the $20 bill and Grant is on the $50 bill.

**Page 112**
**Can You Canoe?**
He doesn't exist. A grandfather, father and son got into the canoe and the son fell out, leaving the grandfather and the father ... who is also a son.

**Page 112**
**Hi Ho Silver**
Friday was the name of Ben's horse.

**130**

**Page 113**
**Talking States**
She died of Missouri.
She wore her New Jersey.
Ida no, but Alaska.

**Page 113**
**Sheila the Great**
Sheila was watching television.

# Solutions

**Page 114**
**Down Under**
South Australia is 18 hours ahead of California. They left on Tuesday at 3:00 p.m. California time and their flight took 15 hours total, so they arrived before they left.

**Page 114**
**Double Trouble**
Salem is the name of a US city in Massachusetts and Oregon. Portland is an incorrect answer since it does not have 17th-century architecture.

**Page 115**
**Birthday Boy**
He was born on February 29th. 1904 was the first leap year after 1896. Normally every four years there is a leap year, but there was no leap year in 1900.

**Page 115**
**Road Trip**
Sacramento, CA
Columbus, OH
Concord, NH
Dover, DE

131

**Page 116**
**Happy Family**
Homer(Of course!)

**Page 116**
**Campfire**
The match

# Solutions

### Page 117
### Bus Stop
3 buses (Each bus holds 50 kids, so two buses hold 100 kids and the third is needed for the extra 25.)

### Page 117
### Time to Go
She was just killing time while she waited for Mr. Rosner, her little lambchop.

### Page 118
### Wide Load
Let air out of the tires (The truck will lower and be able to drive forward.)

### Page 118
### Compass Confusion
East (Los Angeles is actually east of Reno.)

### Page 119
### Phone Tree
45 individual conversations. The formula is $N(n-1) \div 2$, where N is the total number of kids. So $10(10-1) \div 2 = 45$. Another way to do it is to say Maia talked to nine, the next kid talked to eight and add up all the conversations.

### Page 119
### Traveling Abroad
Lon<u>don</u>
Ber<u>lin</u>
<u>Bud</u>apest
<u>P</u>ar<u>is</u>

# Solutions

**Page 120**
**Chirp Chirp**
They are all NFL team names.

**Page 120**
**If I Ran the Zoo**
Detroit, MI (home of the Detroit Tigers and the Detroit Lions)

**Page 121**
**Life's Lessons**
The letter "F"

**Page 121**
**The Getaway**
He's walking.

133

**Page 122**
**Riddle Me This**
A snake

**Page 122**
**Exciting**
I am an envelope.

# Solutions

**Page 123**
**I'm Never Blue**
A banana

**Page 123**
**Who Was That Masked Man?**
Because Elizabeth is playing baseball and the umpire calls her out!

134

**Page 124**
**Out of Touch**
Your lips

**Page 124**
**E-X-T-R-A Credit**
Edinburg and Sarajevo

**Page 125**
**Freezer Burn**
A Popsicle®

**Page 125**
**SSSSSS**
Prince…princes…princess

**Page 126**
**Fur Sure**
The outside, silly!

**Page 126**
**Roll Out the Barrel**
Holes

# 30 Second Mysteries

# The Strange Stranger

### THE CASE
A famous stranger bursts into a house where two children named Conrad and Sally wait alone for their mother. He tries to make the children play games they don't want to play. Eventually the stranger leaves, but the police are not called.

### THE MYSTERY
Who is the stranger and who made him famous?

### THE CLUES
The stranger is wearing a hat, gloves, a bow tie and a fur coat.
A famous Doctor brought him to life, but the stranger is not real.
The stranger's friends are two Things.
The stranger is a cat.

*The stranger is the Cat in the Hat.*
*Dr. Seuss made him famous.*

# Bawling Baldie

### THE CASE
A bald male opens his eyes and finds himself naked in a small room full of people he doesn't recognize. A female grabs him and starts to slap him before he can say anything. The male is shocked and bursts into tears.

### THE MYSTERY
Who is the male and who is the female?

### THE CLUES
The male is not being punished.
The female went to school to learn to treat the male this way.
The male weighs less than 10 pounds.
The male and female are in the hospital.

*The male is a baby and the female is a doctor (obstetrician).*

# Murder and Trickery

### THE CASE
A man finds himself surrounded by mean strangers who want to eat him. He runs away, only to encounter fierce animals and other problems. Finally, he places his trust in a friendly stranger, only to be tricked and murdered.

### THE MYSTERY
Who is the man and who tricked him?

### THE CLUES
The man can't swim, but the stranger can.
The man is irresistibly sweet.
The man tells everyone he can run faster than they can.
The friendly stranger has a very foxy mind.

*The man is the Gingerbread Man, who was eaten by the Fox.*

# A Father Alone

## THE CASE

A father lovingly cares for his baby after its mother has left them. He gives up his own comfort for many months while he protects the child from danger. Finally, the mother comes back and the father immediately goes off to sea, leaving his little one behind.

## THE MYSTERY

Who is this father?

## THE CLUES

Without the father, the child would die almost instantly.
The father knows the mother is coming back.
The father lives with many other fathers in Antarctica.
The father wears only a tuxedo but he is not human.

*The father is a penguin.*

# Body Double?

### THE CASE
On her 16th birthday, Taylor goes to the DMV to get her driver's license. The clerk tells Taylor that earlier that same day another girl with the same birth date, last name and address also got a driver's license. The clerk asks Taylor if she is a twin and she truthfully answers that she is not.

### THE MYSTERY
Who was the other girl and how is she related to Taylor?

### THE CLUES
Taylor knows the other girl very well.
Taylor and her sister celebrate all their birthdays together.
When Taylor was born, her family was in the news.
Taylor's mother knitted three baby blankets during her pregnancy.

*The other girl is Taylor's sister, but they are triplets, not twins.*

# The Brave Lady in the Night

## THE CASE
In the dark of night during the Civil War, a daring woman performed feats that few would even think of. Over many years, she put herself and others in harm's way with her shocking adventures, but in the end she escaped unharmed. After meeting her, people were never the same again.

## THE MYSTERY
Who was this person and what is she famous for?

## THE CLUES
People think of the woman as a great American heroine.
She did her best work in the 1850s and 1860s.
She helped countless people make a safe passage.
She traveled on a "railroad."

*Harriet Tubman is famous for helping to free slaves on the Underground Railroad.*

# The Stranger in the Night

### THE CASE

A woman steals into Ken's room at night, intent on taking at least one thing with her when she leaves. Ken is not aware of this visitor, but would not be afraid if he knew she was there. The woman and Ken have never met.

### THE MYSTERY

Who is this woman and what does she leave?

### THE CLUES

The items the woman takes from Ken are not valuable.
Ken is six years old.
The woman's visit is profitable for Ken.
The woman is not a witch, but she's not human either.

The woman is the Tooth Fairy.
She leaves small sums of money.

# Stalker or Not?

## THE CASE

In downtown Paris, only a thin pane of glass separates an unknown man and a famous woman. The man stares at the woman for nearly three hours. Rather than get annoyed, the woman simply smiles back at him.

## THE MYSTERY

Who is the woman?

## THE CLUES

The woman has no eyebrows.
The woman looks good for her age, which is about 500.
The man is at the Louvre Museum.
The woman was created by the famous painter Leonardo da Vinci.

*The man is looking at the Mona Lisa.*

# The Vanishing Man

## THE CASE
One man's image has inspired many songs, stories and poems. Some have even traveled record-breaking distances to visit him. For as long as anyone can remember, some people have seen him at night. However, he only shows his face from a distance; when people get close, he disappears.

## THE MYSTERY
Who is this man and what part of him are people able to see?

## THE CLUES
He is surrounded by stars, but he's not an actor.
Some people think that he has an unlimited supply of green cheese.
He shows himself when it gets dark out.
People first visited his home in 1969.

*He is the Man in the Moon, whose face people see when gazing into the night sky.*

# The Volunteer with a Secret

### THE CASE
A man keeps responding to emergencies, even though he is not a police officer or firefighter. He provides his own uniform and performs these good deeds without ever being paid.

### THE MYSTERY
Who is the man and what is printed on his uniform?

### THE CLUES
The man changes into his uniform in many different places.
The man is a reporter.
The man's uniform is blue—and it's very tight.
The man can leap tall buildings in a single bound.

*The man's name is Clark Kent (or Superman) and there is an "S" on his uniform.*

# The Puzzling Patriot

### THE CASE

An American patriot traveled on a small horse to a faraway village. When he arrived, he placed part of a bird into his clothing. He then did something very strange, announcing to everyone that he had some Italian pasta with him.

### THE MYSTERY

Who is the patriot, and what is the Italian pasta?

### THE CLUES

The first part of the patriot's name tells you he's from the North, not the South.

His small horse was a pony.

Most people learn about the patriot in a song.

He put a feather in his cap.

*The Patriot is Yankee Doodle Dandy and the pasta is macaroni.*

# The Unique Teacher

### THE CASE
Jessica's foreign language teacher is never absent and is always in a good mood. She even takes Jessica and a bunch of other kids on a field trip every single day of the week. They all practice their foreign language skills while learning how to read a map and stay away from foxes.

### THE MYSTERY
Who is Jessica's teacher and what language does she teach?

### THE CLUES
The teacher always brings a backpack.
They often visit the teacher's Abuela.
The teacher has her own TV show.
The teacher is a child.

*Jessica's teacher is Dora the Explorer.*
*She teaches Spanish.*

# A Fearless Fellow

### THE CASE
Every day of his life, a fellow faces danger, often finding himself staring at the barrel of a gun. His superior mind allows him to escape every time, usually by poking fun at others. When it's all over, he goes to bed underground.

### THE MYSTERY
Who is this rascal?

### THE CLUES
Despite his name, he is not an insect.
Kids have enjoyed him for generations.
His favorite food is carrots.
His favorite catchphrase is, "What's up, Doc?"

*He's Bugs Bunny.*

# Murder for Hire

### THE CASE
Christina is a contract killer, but strangely enough, the police are not interested in arresting her. She is always invited into the very homes where her murders will take place and her work is done in front of witnesses. No one even tries to stop the killings.

### THE MYSTERY
Who is Christina and how does she kill her victims?

### THE CLUES
Christina never uses a gun to kill.
After a year on the job, she's likely killed thousands, maybe even millions.
Christina usually has to wear a mask when she is working.
Christina hates pests.

*Christina is a professional exterminator.*
*She poisons her victims.*

# The Cemetery Speech

### THE CASE
In wartime, a tall man gives a moving speech at a Pennsylvania cemetery. People are sad for the dead, but the man's words make them feel better. Even though he only speaks for about two minutes, the man's words remain important through many generations.

### THE MYSTERY
Who gave this speech and what is it called?

### THE CLUES
The speech took place during the Civil War.
This man was the president, and he was later assassinated.
The speech starts with these words: "Fourscore and seven years ago…"
He gave the speech for the men lost in a famous battle.

*President Lincoln gave the famous speech, called the "Gettysburg Address."*

# Unseen Sam

## THE CASE

Sam has lived in the United States all of his life. He likes the military but doesn't like wars. He works for the government but isn't in politics. Everyone feels they are related to him, but no one has actually met him.

## THE MYSTERY

Who is Sam?

## THE CLUES

He started working during World War I and has been working ever since.
He is always seen on posters pointing at people and telling them, "I Want You …"
He has white hair and a beard and he always wears a hat.
He represents patriotism.

*He is Uncle Sam.*

# Walk This Way

### THE CASE
While taking a midnight stroll, Kareem is viciously attacked. After quickly rubbing something all over his body, the attackers go off into the night. The attackers didn't have weapons, but Kareem has definitely lost some blood.

### THE MYSTERY
Who was attacking Kareem and what drove them away?

### THE CLUES
Kareem killed a few of the attackers with his bare hands.
The protection Kareem used was a lotion.
The attackers are very small and hard to see at night.
His attackers didn't kick or punch, but they did a lot of biting.

152

*Kareem was bitten by mosquitoes.*
*They stayed away after he applied*
*insect repellent.*

# The Secret Gang Leader

### THE CASE

Out on a boat on a foggy night, a gang of teenagers lands on an island that's said to be filled with phantoms and ghosts. Ignoring the spooky islanders, this gang unmasks the villains, climbs into a van and continues on its merry way, roaming the country to solve crimes of all kinds.

### THE MYSTERY

Who is the shortest member of this gang?

### THE CLUES

It's almost impossible to understand what the shortest gang member is saying.

He's only short because he walks on four legs.

He'll do anything for a snack.

His best pal is Shaggy.

The shortest member of this gang is Scooby-Doo.

# Who Was that Masked Man?

### THE CASE
A masked guard is attacked by a gang of five men who shoot at him, then quickly flee. He survives the attack, but the gang returns again and again for 60 minutes before it quits. The next night, a different gang attacks him. The gangs never use guns.

### THE MYSTERY
What is the masked man's profession?

### THE CLUES
The man is very goal-oriented.
The man and his attackers are all wearing uniforms.
The man is in front of a net.
The man is wearing ice skates.

................................................................

*The masked man is a hockey goalie.*

# The Amazing Escape

### THE CASE
A famous man in handcuffs stands on a bridge surrounded by a large group of people. Suddenly, the man leaps off the bridge into the cold, fast-moving river below. Oddly, he does not drown but climbs out of the river safe and sound and is met by an applauding crowd.

### THE MYSTERY
What is the man's name and why did he leap into the river wearing handcuffs?

### THE CLUES
The people watching knew that the man was going to jump into the river.

The man was a famous magician.

The man died in 1926.

The man's last name rhymes with "meanie."

155

*The man was Harry Houdini, who leapt into the river as part of his show business act.*

# The Little Thief

### THE CASE

The young son of a single mother leaves home to trespass on his neighbor's property. While there, he steals from the neighbor and takes off all his clothes before running back home. Although he is seen and chased, he is not caught and no charges are pressed.

### THE MYSTERY

What is the son's name and whose property does he steal?

### THE CLUES

The son has three sisters.

He has large ears and wears only a blue jacket and clogs.

The neighbor doesn't like this little thief in his garden.

The son was created by Beatrix Potter.

**156**

*The son is Peter Rabbit, and he steals Mr. McGregor's vegetables.*

# Round and Round

### THE CASE

Each working day, Celia seems to run in circles to get things done. Instead of becoming frustrated by doing things over and over, she seems to love it. As she sees it, speed is her friend—and the faster she gets through her work, the better.

### THE MYSTERY

What is Celia's job and why doesn't she mind it?

### THE CLUES

To do her job well, Celia really has to put her foot down.

If things get out of control where Celia works, someone could get hurt.

Timing is everything in her line of work.

Her work outfit includes a helmet and a jumpsuit.

*Celia is a racecar driver who loves circling the track.*

# The Frequent Flier

### THE CASE
Zoe travels all over the world for free without ever buying a plane ticket or paying for a hotel. She travels quickly—in some cases she visits three different continents in a single week. She works in every country that she visits, but only gets paid in one.

### THE MYSTERY
What is Zoe's occupation and what type of company does she work for?

### THE CLUES
The company Zoe works for requires its employees to wear uniforms.

Zoe has really taken off in her career.

Zoe doesn't stay long in any one place.

Zoe has wings pinned on her uniform.

158

*Zoe is a pilot who works for an airline.*

# The Uncaged Creature

### THE CASE
A man captures a wild animal and brings it back to civilization. When left alone, the animal often gets into trouble and the man must set things right. Luckily, when the animal looks for the man, his special clothing makes him easy to spot.

### THE MYSTERY
What special clothing does the man wear and what is the animal's name?

### THE CLUES
The animal's first name is an adjective that also means "inquisitive."
The man always wears a hat.
You can read about the animal in books.
The animal likes to monkey around.

*The man always wears a big yellow hat; the animal is Curious George.*

# The Unusual Herd

### THE CASE
A group of men takes care of a large number of horses. People come from miles around to watch them. The horses run all day and into the night, stopping only for short breaks. The men never feed the horses, even though they are their sole source of income.

### THE MYSTERY
What type of horses are they?

### THE CLUES
The horses never stray far from their home and always follow the same path.
The horses have endured for many years.
Riding the horses can have its ups and downs.
The horses travel in circles.

*The horses are carousel horses.*

# It's a Tough Job, But ...

### THE CASE
Todd puts on makeup and a strange outfit to prepare for work. His job makes some people laugh, but those he works with just want to kill him. Though Todd always wears crazy clothes, he really only wants one individual to pay attention to him while he's working.

### THE MYSTERY
What does Todd do for a living and whose attention does he want?

### THE CLUES
Todd often uses a barrel in his work.
Todd works with animals, but they're not trained to do tricks.
Todd doesn't work in Hollywood, but he still deals with a lot of bull.
Todd gets a lot dustier than most clowns.

**161**

*Todd works as a rodeo clown who tries to distract the bull from the fallen rider.*

# Austin's Odd Occupation

### THE CASE

Austin is a government worker who spends his whole day sitting down. Customers pay money and then watch him sit. Austin ignores these customers while he looks outside his office window. If Austin does his job right, the customers leave as soon as he is finished.

### THE MYSTERY

What is Austin's job?

### THE CLUES

Austin wears a uniform while he works.

Unless it's a very busy day, the customers stay seated while they are with Austin.

When the customers leave Austin they are on the street.

Austin is driving a vehicle.

*Austin is a bus driver.*

# The Unusual Explosions

### THE CASE
Mary straps her son Nicholas into a machine and then casually turns it on. After a series of explosions, Mary turns off the machine, unstraps Nicholas and leaves the machine behind. Neither Mary, Nicholas nor the machine are harmed.

### THE MYSTERY
What type of machine is this?

### THE CLUES
Mary owns the machine.
The explosions are mechanically controlled and are perfectly normal.
Mary needs a hand-held tool to get into the machine and to turn it on.
The machine was made by Ford.

*The machine is a car. (The small explosions in the engine are what make it run.)*

# A Weird Career

### THE CASE
Sara must be very careful coming and going from her workplace each day, because it can be very dangerous. Once at work, she sits all alone in the same spot and stares out the window. She does not change her position much during the day—but change is a big part of her job.

### THE MYSTERY
What is Sara's job?

### THE CLUES
The view from Sara's window changes all the time.
People give her money all day, but she cannot spend it.
People roll down their windows to talk to Sara.
She works at a bridge, but she might want to transfer to a turnpike someday.

*Sara is a toll collector.*

# The Lost Letter

### THE CASE
Brandon asks Aisha for her address to send her a letter. Aisha checks the mail every day but the letter never comes. She later finds out that Brandon was involved in a crash and could not get the letter to her. Brandon is not injured and there is no damage to his car.

### THE MYSTERY
What happened to Brandon, and whose fault was it?

### THE CLUES
Aisha received all of her other mail.
The address Aisha gave Brandon did not include a zip code.
The crash happened at Brandon's desk and it didn't make any noise.
Aisha's address had the word "Yahoo" in it.

*Brandon had Aisha's email address and his computer crashed. It was no one's fault.*

# Unparked Parker

## THE CASE

Parker travels over 200 miles in a day, yet he is home for dinner every night. He rarely sees the same people from one day to the next, but he is almost never alone. He stops his vehicle often, but Parker rarely parks.

## THE MYSTERY

What is Parker doing and what color is his vehicle?

## THE CLUES

Parker works in a big city.
Parker is not afraid to use his horn.
Parker charges by the mile.
Parker drives a car with a sign on the top.

*Parker is driving a taxi;*
*his vehicle is yellow.*

166

# The Price of Fame

## THE CASE
The stars of a TV show are upset that they were chosen. They will probably not be on the next episode or, if they are, it will be their last appearance. They do not audition for the show—they are chosen by the producers to be seen by America.

## THE MYSTERY
What is this TV show?

## THE CLUES
The audience doesn't vote, but the producers hope they'll call in.
The host of the show continually asks America for its help.
The show is nonfiction. All the characters are real.
The show helps the FBI catch criminals.

The show is
America's Most Wanted.

# Is Curtis Crazy?

### THE CASE
Curtis carries a book of matches in his pocket. Every night, he walks into a room full of people, takes out the book of matches and amazes every person in the crowd. Curtis hears gasps, sighs and then applause, but he can't speak while the audience is reacting.

### THE MYSTERY
What is Curtis's profession?

### THE CLUES
It's likely that no one else in the crowd can do what Curtis can.
Curtis's mouth is full while he works.
Curtis is an entertainer and his act is hot stuff.
Curtis is carefully trained in pyrotechnics.

**168**

*Curtis is a fire eater.*

# Harsh Judgment

### THE CASE
Michelle slowly slides her fingers against the silver blades in her hand to check their sharpness. Next, she looks in the mirror and prepares to be judged by a group of people from around the world. Michelle will not enter a courtroom, yet the group's judgment may affect both her and her country.

### THE MYSTERY
What is Michelle doing?

### THE CLUES
Michelle does not walk or talk in front of the group.
She is surrounded by ice, yet Michelle wears very little.
This is Michelle's golden opportunity.
Music plays while Michelle is in front of the group.

*Michelle is a figure skater competing for a gold medal.*

# A Mysterious Hero

### THE CASE

An entire town watches a man in uniform save hundreds of lives every day. The hero has a special sign that gives him this life-saving power. He is an elderly man with white hair and a slow step, yet he can stop a fast-moving truck with one hand.

### THE MYSTERY

What do people call this man and what is the symbol that gives him his power?

### THE CLUES

He can stop all kinds of vehicles, but he can't stop a speeding bullet.
Most kids know him well, but he's not in the movies or comic books.
His sign is a red octagon and his uniform is an orange vest.
He works at an intersection.

*The man is a crossing guard who uses a stop sign to control traffic.*

# The Reckless Driver

## THE CASE

Thirteen-year-old David drives a car for several hours before tiring. He sees several police officers and often exceeds 100 miles per hour. David never pays for gas and ignores most traffic signs, yet he is not pulled over and he doesn't get a ticket.

## THE MYSTERY

What is David doing?

## THE CLUES

David and his brother take turns driving.

David crashes the car several times.

The car runs on electricity.

David finally stops the car when his thumbs get tired.

*David is playing a video game.*

# Ben There, Done That

### THE CASE

Ben has a high profile and an easy-to-recognize face. People all over town look up to him. Guards protect his home 24 hours a day while Ben entertains visitors, poses for pictures and provides a valuable service without any worries at all.

### THE MYSTERY

Where does Ben live and what service does he provide?

### THE CLUES

Ben depends on his hands and face.
Ben is English.
Ben is not a person.
People expect Ben to always be on time.

(Big) Ben tells time in London.

172

# The Confounding Corpse

## THE CASE
A man's body is found in California, 1,000 feet below sea level.
He's dead, but drowning is not the cause of death. The spot
where the man lost his life is well known as a killer place to be.

## THE MYSTERY
Where and how did the man die?

## THE CLUES
The man was not near the ocean when he died.
Water would have saved the man's life.
The man died in the desert.
The man died in a valley named for its deadly heat.

*The man died from the heat in Death Valley.*

# What's Cory's Story?

### THE CASE
A steady stream of people enter Cory's workplace and remove treasured belongings. The people do not pay for what they take. Cory allows them to take as much as they want as long as they keep it quiet.

### THE MYSTERY
Where does Cory work and what are the people taking?

### THE CLUES
Cory is more of a lender than a seller.
Cory works in a public place that is run by the city.
Cory sometimes thinks of his customers as a kind of worm.
Sometimes Cory makes people pay when they bring the belongings back late.

Cory works for a library; people are taking (or checking out) books.

# Where's Wyatt?

## THE CASE
Wyatt rides his bike out of a big city. As he travels, he sees water on either side of him and two orange towers above him. After about 15 minutes Wyatt stops, turns around and admires a tall pyramid.

## THE MYSTERY
Where has Wyatt stopped?

## THE CLUES
It is foggy, but Wyatt can see an old prison on an island in the distance.
On the right side of Wyatt is a bay; on his left is the Pacific Ocean.
Wyatt rode past a tollbooth.
Wyatt is in San Francisco.

*Wyatt has stopped on the Golden Gate Bridge.*

# The Huge Hole

## THE CASE

Four reddened people walk to the edge of a hole, where they stop and gaze in. This starts to make them dizzy, so they look out (not down) at the rocks before them. Soon, they climb onto animals and begin their long journey into the hole.

## THE MYSTERY

Where are these people?

## THE CLUES

The animals are burros.
The people are sunburned because this place gets pretty hot.
The hole is one mile deep and has been a national park since 1919.
It's located in Arizona.

**176**

*They are in the Grand Canyon.*

# The Frightened Captive

## THE CASE

A boy who is all alone is taken to a seat by a woman in uniform. She is a stranger to him, but she straps him to the seat. He cries but is told to be quiet and sit still. Hours later, the boy is freed and is told he may leave. He doubts that he will ever see the woman again.

## THE MYSTERY

Where is the boy and who is the woman?

## THE CLUES

The woman is just doing her job.

The boy's parents are waiting outside for him when he leaves.

While they are together, the woman feeds the boy and gives him headphones.

When the boy leaves the woman in uniform, he is in a different city than the one he met her in.

*The boy is on an airplane.*
*The woman is a flight attendant.*

# The Trip to Nowhere

## THE CASE
On a three-day weekend in May, Moss hops into his car in Indiana and begins to drive. He drives for hours in one direction, going hundreds of miles. When Moss stops the car and gets out, he's still in Indiana. In fact, he's in the same place that he started.

## THE MYSTERY
Where is Moss?

## THE CLUES
Moss drove in this state last year at the same time.
Moss is doing his job.
Moss is in Indiana's capital city.
Moss often drives more than 100 miles per hour without getting a speeding ticket.

*Moss is driving in the Indianapolis 500 Race.*

# Thanks, But No Thanks

### THE CASE
A man enters a sweepstakes and is notified by mail that he has won third prize: a new refrigerator. The man has a home, but does not have a fridge. Even though there are no hidden costs and he needs to keep his family's food cold, he turns down the prize.

### THE MYSTERY
Where in the US does the man live and what is his home called?

### THE CLUES
The man is a fisherman who built his house by himself.
The man's home is white.
The man lives in the largest US state.
The man usually uses snow to keep his food cold.

*The man lives in Alaska in an igloo.*

# Julio's Home

## THE CASE

Julio is an American citizen born in 1996. He has never been out of the country, but he has also never entered a single US state. He could easily take a bus to two of them but he just hasn't gotten around to it yet.

## THE MYSTERY

Where does Julio live?

## THE CLUES

Julio lives on the North American continent.
Julio lives in a capital city.
Julio lives near the Smithsonian Institution and Capitol Hill.
The two states near Julio's house are Virginia and Maryland.

*Julio lives in Washington D.C.*

# It Came from Underground

### THE CASE

The ground beneath a group of unsuspecting people gurgles and groans. Steam escapes from a hole nearby and suddenly a violent sound bursts out, followed by an amazing white-hot display of force. Instead of running for their lives, the people step closer and gaze in wonder.

### THE MYSTERY

Where are these people?

### THE CLUES

This display can be seen about once an hour.
It can reach heights of 106–184 feet.
It can be seen in Yellowstone National Park.
In 1870, this natural attraction was named for its reliable performance.

They are visiting the Old Faithful geyser.

# Leadfoot Lydia

### THE CASE
Hughes Bank has just been robbed! Two miles from the bank, Lydia is racing down the highway. She has not committed a crime, but three police cars are hot on her trail. Lydia does not pull over—and continues to speed through traffic with the police following her every move.

### THE MYSTERY
Where is Lydia heading and what is her profession?

### THE CLUES
Lydia will continue at top speed until she reaches her destination.

Lydia is not breaking the law and knows the names of all the police officers following her.

Lydia carries a revolver and a club, and she won't hesitate to use them.

Lydia wears a badge.

*Lydia is a police officer heading toward Hughes Bank.*

# Miserable Isabel?

### THE CASE
Every morning before sunrise, Isabel leaves her apartment and goes to sit in a small room all by herself. In the room, she listens to music and talks out loud for four hours. Isabel is alone the whole time, but she is not considered crazy, and she even gets paid for this strange behavior.

### THE MYSTERY
Where does Isabel go every night and why is she there?

### THE CLUES
The room is occupied 24 hours a day.
Isabel is wearing headphones and the room is sound proof.
Isabel isn't talking to herself.
If the people listening to Isabel want to talk to her, they have to call in.

*Isabel is a disc jockey and she is in the room to host her late-night radio show.*

# Where's Claire?

### THE CASE

Claire watches a group of men standing below her. She sees one of the men get caught trying to steal, while another just stands by and does nothing. Suddenly, the people around her stand up, stretch their legs and begin to sing. Claire quickly joins in.

### THE MYSTERY

Where is Claire and what does the crowd sing?

### THE CLUES

Claire has been sitting in the same place for two hours.
Claire's brother and dad are sitting next to her and are both wearing the same hats.
Claire ate a hot dog and a box of Cracker Jack® an hour earlier.
The song includes the words, "Root, root, root for the home team."

**184**

*Claire is at a baseball game. The crowd sings*
*"Take Me Out to the Ball Game."*

# Watch Your Step

### THE CASE

Maria takes small, careful steps every night, often using a stick to help her along. Strangers watch her, but no one ever offers to help. The threat of Maria stumbling causes some people to shield their eyes.

### THE MYSTERY

Where is Maria working and what is she doing?

### THE CLUES

Maria isn't sick or old.

Maria really looks down on her audience.

Flashy outfits make up most of her wardrobe.

Her job requires amazing balance.

*Maria works at the circus walking a tightrope.*

# The International Man of Mystery

### THE CASE
A man who is known by many different names has an international reputation, but he has never been seen. Occasionally, he dashes out under the cover of night. His home is very remote and nearly impossible to reach.

### THE MYSTERY
Where is the man's home and what is he called in the US?

### THE CLUES
The man is old, but age doesn't slow him down.
The man usually wears a suit.
The man has never been on a plane, but he has flown all over the world.
The man employs little helpers to carry out his business.

*The man lives at the North Pole and he is called Santa Claus.*

# Lucky Chuck

### THE CASE

Chuck spends his time going door to door, performing icky tasks all day. He likes helping people and doesn't mind when he has to go to the hospital. Some people treat him badly, but others are nice. Whatever their mood, they all call on him when the going gets tough.

### THE MYSTERY

Where does Chuck work and how does he earn his living?

### THE CLUES

Chuck really knows people, inside and out.
Emergencies happen every day where Chuck works.
Most of the people Chuck helps are lying down.
A stethoscope hangs around his neck, but Chuck is not a doctor.

*Chuck works at a hospital as a nurse.*

# The Strange Chamber

## THE CASE

Erin enters a large building. She is stopped by a man in uniform and is asked to prove her identity or leave the building. Erin is taken to a machine where her belongings are inspected and some items are taken from her. She then eats a sandwich and waits in a high security area until she can leave.

## THE MYSTERY

Where is Erin and what is she waiting for?

## THE CLUES

The room Erin sits in features lots of chairs and a giant window.

One of the items taken from Erin is a pair of scissors.

Erin is waiting in New York, but she is very worried about reports of a storm in London.

About 10 minutes after she leaves the building, Erin is flying high.

*Erin is at the airport waiting for a flight to London.*

# Not a Typical Trip

### THE CASE
A group of four comes together to follow a road to a person they believe will cure all their problems. The group's leader brings along a trusted companion. The group runs into alien animals and develops terrible allergies before they finally reach their destination, which is a real gem of a city.

### THE MYSTERY
Where does the road end and what is the name of the leader's companion?

### THE CLUES
You won't find the city on any map.
The companion sometimes walks and is sometimes carried in a basket.
The companion has four legs.
The road is made of yellow bricks.

The road ends at the Emerald City and the companion's name is Toto.

# Does Anyone Love Lucy?

### THE CASE

Lucy is suffering from a dangerous disease. Her family decides that she should undergo an operation, but Lucy is not told about it. The operation will be performed by someone who has never operated on a human being before.

### THE MYSTERY

Why isn't Lucy told about her operation, and who operates on her?

### THE CLUES

Lucy was adopted and her family loves her very much.
Lucy has a license, but it's not a driver's license.
The person who operates on Lucy has a medical degree but is not a medical doctor.
Lucy is the family's "best friend."

Lucy is a dog. A veterinary surgeon operates on her.

# The Mystery Mouse

### THE CASE
Zack is allergic to most animals and avoids them whenever he can. Nevertheless, he owns a small mouse. He spends several hours every day holding or stroking his mouse, even though he doesn't love it.

### THE MYSTERY
Why isn't Zack allergic to his mouse?

### THE CLUES
Zack does not keep his mouse in a cage.
Zack's mouse does not move unless he pushes it.
Zack's mouse does not eat or drink.
Zack's mouse has a nice pad.

*Zack isn't allergic to his mouse because it's a computer mouse.*

# Poison Ivy?

## THE CASE

Ivy learns that an overweight man needs surgery. She is not a doctor, but she agrees to perform the procedure. She carefully removes the body parts from her patient, including several major organs. He does not die and Ivy does not get in trouble.

## THE MYSTERY

Why is Ivy allowed to do this?

## THE CLUES

Ivy does the surgery free of charge.
Ivy has a very steady hand and uses only tweezers.
If Ivy makes a mistake, she will hear a buzz.
The patient is a man named Sam.

*Ivy is playing the game Operation®.*

# The Brutal Beating

## THE CASE

A small, defenseless animal stands quietly in the sunshine. Suddenly, it is pulled up into the air by a rope and hit over and over with sticks until its body is crushed. Although many witness this beating, no one is punished.

## THE MYSTERY

Why did this action take place?

## THE CLUES

The action took place at a party.
Those who hit the animal could not see it.
Those who hit the animal were children.
The animal was beaten for what was inside it.

*The animal is a piñata being broken open at a party.*

# The Real Estate Caper

## THE CASE

Nina and Maia are making a fortune in real estate. Even though Nina never breaks the law, she is sent to jail several times. Maia follows the same procedures as Nina with many of the same properties, but she never goes to jail.

## THE MYSTERY

Why did Nina go to jail?

## THE CLUES

Nina was sent to jail without a trial.

Nina never left her home when she went to jail. In fact, she never even got out of her chair.

All Nina needs is a good roll, not parole.

Nina did not collect $200 on her way to jail.

*Nina is playing Monopoly® and landed on the square that says, "Go to Jail."*

# The Incredible Escape

### THE CASE
Jake is being chased by a buffalo stampede when he comes to a wide, deep river. To escape, he must cross the river, but there is no bridge and he has no boat. He cannot even swim. He easily gets away and although the river is full, he doesn't even get wet.

### THE MYSTERY
Why is Jake able to cross the river and why don't the buffalo follow?

### THE CLUES
Jake uses no equipment or tools to cross the river.
The buffalo are excellent swimmers.
The buffalo weigh over 1,000 pounds each, but Jake weighs only 100 pounds.
It is wintertime.

Jake can cross the river because it is frozen; the buffalo are too heavy to follow.

# Gone without a Trace

### THE CASE
Sue is a talented sculptor. She crafts beautiful pieces that weigh hundreds of pounds and carefully delivers them to her clients. Within 24 hours of delivery, every sculpture disappears. Sue does not seem to be upset by these disappearances.

### THE MYSTERY
Why isn't Sue upset and what happens to the sculptures?

### THE CLUES
The sculptures haven't been stolen.
Sue must work quickly.
The sculptures may be heat or light sensitive.
The sculptures are clear and cold.

*Sue is an ice sculptor; her sculptures melt.*

# A Matter of Degrees

### THE CASE

A man from Chicago puts on shorts and a tank top, then goes outside in the middle of winter. The wind is blowing and it's 30° outside, but the man is happy that he's not bundled up for the winter like the rest of the people in Chicago.

### THE MYSTERY

Why can the man tolerate the weather and what is he doing?

### THE CLUES

The man is completely comfortable.
The man is far from his work and home.
Everyone else around the man is dressed as he is.
The man is on vacation.

*The man took a trip to a place where the temperature is 30° Celsius.*

# The Baffling Crash

### THE CASE

Bob and Ursula are talking while Bob drives their little two-seater sports car down a winding road. Bob has a seat belt on, but Ursula does not. Suddenly, a truck hits their car. Bob has two broken legs and a broken pelvis, but Ursula doesn't have a scratch. Ursula calls the police right away, but can't tell them where the accident happened.

### THE MYSTERY

Why isn't Ursula injured and why doesn't she know where the accident occurred?

### THE CLUES

There was equal damage on the driver's and passenger's side of the car.
Ursula was not wearing any special protection.
Ursula has good vision, but she never saw the truck coming.
Ursula could hear Bob, but she couldn't see him.

..........................................................................................................

*Ursula was not in the car; she was talking to Bob on his cell phone.*

# Foolish Jules

### THE CASE
Jules is the guest of honor at a party where he downs seven drinks in three hours. Despite warnings from his friends, he runs outside, hops into the bright red sports car parked in the driveway and drives away. Minutes later, he crashes into a tree and totals the car. The police test Jules's blood and find no alcohol.

### THE MYSTERY
Why were the test results negative and why did Jules have the accident?

### THE CLUES
The test results were accurate, but Jules did break the law.
Jules' drink of choice is bubbly and probably gave him a sugar high.
The accident was on October 4, 2003. Jules was born on October 4, 1988.
Jules did not drink any alcohol at the party.

*Jules was drinking soda, but he was only 15 years old and didn't know how to drive.*

# A Case of Pace

### THE CASE

An elderly woman goes for a nice, slow walk. Two young men in great shape are right behind her, sprinting toward her. No matter how fast they run, they do not catch up with the woman.

### THE MYSTERY

Why can't the men catch up with the woman?

### THE CLUES

The men are running as fast as they can.

The men always stay seven feet behind the woman.

All three people paid money to be where they are.

All three people are indoors.

*All three people are on treadmills in a gym.*

# The Captive Competitor

## THE CASE

Chip is an athlete who is never allowed to leave his home alone, even though he is an adult. When he does get out, under strict supervision, thousands of people come to watch him compete. Chip is in excellent health and has no known mental problems. He is well cared for and never complains about his living arrangements.

## THE MYSTERY

Why doesn't Chip complain and what is his profession?

## THE CLUES

Chip is a professional, yet he earns no money for himself.

Chip follows his instincts when he competes.

Even if Chip wanted to complain about being kept on such a tight leash, he couldn't really say anything.

Chip loves to go to the racetrack.

Chip is a greyhound and he competes in dog races.

# The Peculiar Purse Snatching

### THE CASE
Emily is sitting in a chair reading a book when a man bursts into her room and snatches her purse from right in front of her. He carries no weapon, but Emily does not stop him. She reports the crime to the police, giving a description of her purse but no details about the man.

### THE MYSTERY
Why didn't Emily stop the man?

### THE CLUES
Emily did not know the man, but she knew he was breaking into her home.
Emily speaks only English, but her book was written in another language.
Emily's hands were busy at the time of the break-in.
Emily did not see the man.

*Emily is blind and was reading a book in Braille.*

# The Doctor of Doom?

### THE CASE

Dr. Cooper goes into surgery and immediately passes out. The operation is finished by the time he comes to. After a few days, he operates on a sick child. Even though the hospital knows that the child will die if Dr. Cooper passes out again, he is allowed to operate unsupervised.

### THE MYSTERY

Why did Dr. Cooper pass out and why is he trusted to perform the operation on the child?

### THE CLUES

Dr. Cooper's operation on the sick child was a success.
It did not surprise anyone that Dr. Cooper passed out.
Dr. Cooper was not operating when he passed out.
Dr. Cooper was lying down when he passed out.

*Dr. Cooper passed out because he was given anesthesia; he can operate now that he is recovered from his surgery.*

# Peter's Peculiar Pictures

### THE CASE

In addition to pictures of his wife and children, Peter carries pictures of dead people with him at all times. Peter admires the people, but they are not members of his family. Even though some of the pictures are very valuable, Peter often gives the pictures away.

### THE MYSTERY

Why does Peter carry the pictures and why does he give them away?

### THE CLUES

The fewer pictures Peter gives away, the better he feels.
The pictures are wallet-sized.
Peter trades the pictures for things that he wants.
Peter's favorite picture is a green portrait of Benjamin Franklin.

*Peter carries the pictures because they are money, which he exchanges for the things he buys.*

# A Frightening Fall

### THE CASE

Connie hugs her children tightly and kisses them goodbye.
As she steps out the door, she falls and screams. Her children
watch in horror as she flails about, but they do nothing to
help her. Within an hour, they are all one big happy family
again and talk about the fall over lunch.

### THE MYSTERY

Why did Connie fall and why didn't the children help her?

### THE CLUES

Connie wasn't hurt by the fall.

The children couldn't have reached their mom even if
they wanted to.

Connie fell thousands of feet, but had a soft landing.

The door Connie walked through was on an airplane.

*Connie jumped out of a plane.*
*The children didn't help because she had a parachute.*

# The Untouched Ice Cream

### THE CASE

An ice cream stand offers free giant sundaes at sunset during the summer. At the end of the summer, the owner reviews his records and finds that, even though he had many customers, not one sundae was given away. He is not surprised.

### THE MYSTERY

Why doesn't the owner ever have to give away any sundaes?

### THE CLUES

The customers laughed when they read the offer.

The ice cream stand is in Alaska.

In 20 years of business, the owner has never given away a sundae. And he never will.

The ice cream stand only makes this offer during the summer, when the days are very long.

*The owner never has to give away any sundaes because the sun never sets in Alaska during the summer months.*

# Terrible Tea

## THE CASE

George attends a party, where he quickly gulps down a large iced tea in under a minute before having to leave unexpectedly. He suffers no ill effects, but other people at the party who drink the iced tea are poisoned and get very sick.

## THE MYSTERY

Why did the other people become ill and why didn't George?

## THE CLUES

All the iced teas were exactly the same, and everyone drank an equal amount.

The tea itself wasn't poisoned, but something else in the glass was.

The iced teas looked completely normal.

The poison was frozen.

*The ice in the drinks was poisoned; George drank his iced tea before the ice melted.*

# A Man's Castle

### THE CASE

A man builds a castle but never lives in it, despite its popularity.
Even after his death, millions visit it every year, encountering
enormous beasts and witnessing terrible explosions. Though
exhausted and drained of valuable resources, many feel
compelled to take another journey to the castle's grounds
in the future.

### THE MYSTERY

Who built the castle and where is it?

### THE CLUES

A TV and movie producer designed the castle.
The castle is part of a magical place in California.
The castle is surrounded by an amusement park.
The castle's creator brought Pinocchio to life.

*Walt Disney built the castle as part of Disneyland.*

# Visiting Day

### THE CASE

Parents willingly take their children to visit an eccentric middle-aged man in his extravagant residence. They do not know the man and are very anxious about entering his home. Once inside, they must save their children from near disaster as a result of spending time with this man. Still, he is never charged with a single crime.

### THE MYSTERY

Who is the man and where does he live?

### THE CLUES

The children are all contest winners.
The man offers the parents and their kids a sweet deal.
Roald Dahl wrote a book about the man.
The man loves chocolate.

*The man is Willy Wonka. He lives in a chocolate factory.*

# A Boy Wonder

### THE CASE

A widow gives birth to a son with a slight deformity. Many in her community cruelly taunt and torment her son. When the widow tries to defend him, she is imprisoned. However, as the son gets older, he discovers his deformity has given him an unusual ability that leads to fame and fortune.

### THE MYSTERY

What is the son's deformity and what special ability does he have?

### THE CLUES

The son does not discover his unusual ability until he drinks something.

A magic feather gives the son confidence in himself.

The widow's husband was named Jumbo.

Mother and son are both Disney characters.

*The son is Dumbo, an elephant born with enormous ears. The ears give him the ability to fly.*

# Scary Monster

### THE CASE

Thousands of people stand in the middle of a city street and look up into the sky at an enormous wild creature. The yellow creature hovers over the crowd and dives toward a group of schoolchildren standing near a famous department store. A group of men struggles to contain the creature with nets and ropes, hoping desperately to keep it from attacking the crowd.

### THE MYSTERY

What is the creature's name and where can it be found?

### THE CLUES

There are other strange creatures flying in the same area.
The crowd has gathered for a national holiday.
The creature is big and feathery and lives on a famous street.
Everyone thinks these creatures are full of hot air.

**211**

*The creature is Big Bird as a balloon float. It can be found at Macy's Thanksgiving Day Parade in New York City.*

# A Fight to the Death

## THE CASE

A group of desperate men takes refuge in a nearby church. The enemy approaches and the men are vastly outnumbered. A standoff ensues that lasts nearly two weeks. When the scuffle is over, all the men from the church are defeated and dead, but people think of them as heroes, not lunatics.

## THE MYSTERY

Where in the United States can this church be found and what is its name?

## THE CLUES

It's a well-preserved historic site.
It figured in the battle for one state's independence.
The enemy spoke Spanish.
It can be found in the Lone Star State.

*It is the Alamo in San Antonio, Texas.*

# In the Dark

### THE CASE
Vito leads a group of people into a dark room that's filled with a very strong smell. The people are supposed to be silent the entire time they are in the room. If they speak too often or too loudly, Vito scolds them.

### THE MYSTERY
Where are the people and what is Vito's job?

### THE CLUES
The people often laugh or cry.
The smell is fresh and buttery!
The people have paid to sit in the room.
The people will leave the room after about two hours.

*The people are in a movie theater and Vito is a theater usher.*

# The Greedy Ones

### THE CASE

At night in a quiet neighborhood, mobs of people move through the streets, using threats to get stuff from the people who live there. Although they continue their behavior for several hours, no one reports them to the authorities or even complains.

### THE MYSTERY

Why are these people moving through the streets and what threat do they make?

### THE CLUES

Many of the people are frightening to look at.
The residents knew ahead of time that this would happen.
The people are not doing anything illegal.
This is an annual event that takes place every October.

*The people are children in Halloween costumes who want candy when they say, "Trick or treat!"*

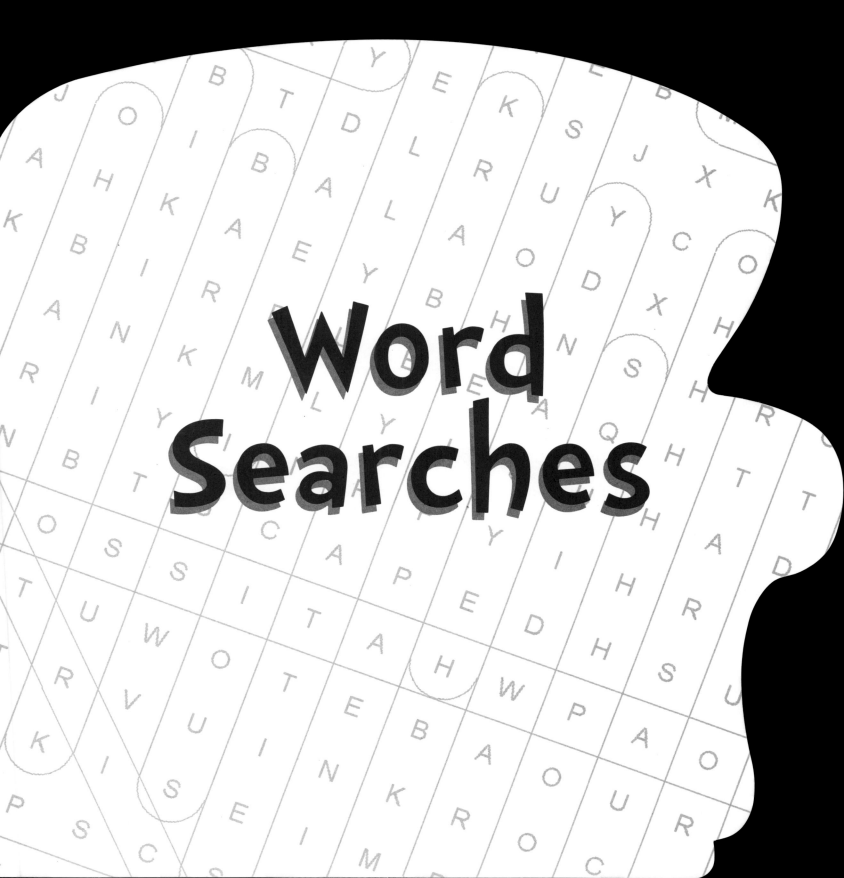

# Word Searches

# Animal Talk

| | | |
|---|---|---|
| BEAR HUG | CASH COW | MONKEY BUSINESS |
| BEELINE | CATWALK | PIGGYBACK |
| BIRD BRAIN | COPYCAT | PUPPY LOVE |
| BLACK SHEEP | DEAD DUCK | SAWHORSE |
| BULLDOZER | HOT DOG | SCAPEGOAT |
| BULLPEN | JAILBIRD | STOOL PIGEON |

M E U F T A C Y P O C K B K W
O Q N J P M A C A S H C O W B
N P H F E V O L Y P P U P I I
K L V G E V A A B C N D I P E
E S R O H W A S E O J D F C A
Y V G B S C A P E G O A T K B
B L D U K U P G L U O E F U X
U I Q L C T I T I H N D L C I
S T R L A P G O N R C L T F E
I K N D L D G B E A P U A O C
N R J O B T Y U T E T T J R H
E P O Z A R B W N B L Q N E
S T N E Z J A I L B I R D
S M I R V L C I C Y Y H
M L I B K I K E N Q N

# Boys Will Be Boys

| | | |
|---|---|---|
| BILL NYE | JIMMY NEUTRON | SHAGGY |
| BING AND BONG | LOUIS STEVENS | SHREK |
| CATDOG | MICKEY MOUSE | SPONGEBOB |
| CHUCKY | MR. WHISKERS | STITCH |
| CODY BANKS | NEMO | TOM AND JERRY |
| ED, EDD 'N EDDY | SCOOBY DOO | TOMMY |

Wacky Word Games • Word Searches

```
G  L  Y  K  B  L  I  M  P  S  X  V  R  Z  N
E  E  R  K  D  Z  G  E  Y  N  L  L  I  B  A
Q  J  T  B  Q  E  O  Y  S  J  Q  E  I  G  T
B  L  O  U  I  S  S  T  E  V  E  N  S  H  O
T  O  M  M  Y  C  A  T  D  O  G  V  P  T  M
K  O  A  S  C  O  D  Y  B  A  N  K  S  Y  E
T  D  N  J  I  M  M  Y  N  E  U  T  R  O  N
G  Y  D  D  E  N  D  D  E  D  E  W  R  T  Y
X  B  J  W  L  J  B  O  B  E  G  N  O  P  S
L  O  E  S  U  O  M  Y  E  K  C  I  M  Z  O
S  O  R  Y  N  K  O  Y  G  G  A  H  S  W  P
P  C  R  G  M  R  W  H  I  S  K  E  R  S
R  S  Y  K  C  U  H  C  T  I  T  S  B
S  H  R  E  K  K  A  Q  U  M  D  M
```

SOLUTION FOUND ON PAGE 312.

219

# Bust a Move!

ANDALE!

BEAT IT

BOLT

BUST A MOVE

FLOOR IT

GET IN GEAR

GET SHAKIN'

HIGHTAIL IT

JET

LET'S BAIL

LET'S BOOGIE

LET'S FLY

LET'S ROLL

MAKE LIKE A TREE

MAKE TRACKS

MOTOR

LATER

MOVE IT

PEDAL TO THE METAL

SCOOT

SCRAM

SKEDADDLE

VAMANOS

VAMOOSE

Wacky Word Games • Word Searches

```
B  R  R  J  B  A  K  B  O  L  T  T  E  J  Y
V  M  O  C  H  G  M  O  V  E  I  T  L  L  V
L  A  T  E  M  E  H  T  O  T  L  A  D  E  P
G  K  O  A  O  T  B  R  A  S  I  V  D  T  E
A  E  M  S  M  I  I  E  E  B  A  A  A  S  J
P  L  T  A  K  N  B  O  U  O  T  M  D  R  V
A  I  O  S  K  G  A  S  U  O  H  O  E  O  X
P  K  L  F  H  E  T  G  I  G  G  O  K  L  H
M  E  S  L  L  A  T  E  R  I  I  S  S  L  U
T  A  Y  O  M  R  K  R  P  E  H  E  E  J  Q
H  T  D  O  N  W  L  I  A  B  S  T  E  L  M
J  R  V  R  M  A  T  A  N  C  S  C  S  O
Y  E  A  I  T  P  M  L  R  F  K  P  N
T  E  H  T  A  N  D  A  L  E  Y  S
S  C  O  O  T  N  M  Y  V  Z  U
```

SOLUTION FOUND ON PAGE 313.

**221**

# Butter, Bugs and Bears

*Try reading each column out loud from top to bottom as fast as you can*
*before you start your search. Now, do it again. And again. And again! Faster!*

| | | |
|---|---|---|
| BETTY | SHE SAID | BITE |
| BOTTER | THIS BATCH IS | BROWN |
| BOUGHT | BITTER. | BEARS' |
| A BUCKET | BIG | BUTTS |
| OF BUTTER | BLACK | BRINGING |
| BUT | BUGS | BOO BOOS. |

A A W H R R M O Z S D U E Y E

M B E B K U X C A L Q W Q T H

B S E B U B G D I Y O T I T U

C G N Y L P V M Z G. H B H E R

Z D A W X B G N I G N I R B Z

U V A V O K P B U G S T T U B

B O T T E R A O F B U T T E R

Y Q B W E J B L A C K E S M U

C J L U A K Q T B S E R R H L

M K W X U G C X O H A B I H M

Z K M F A H I U O E V K J O I

L Q D P I Y M J B S Z F B Y

O M X S B A E Y O A L H O

U L X V Z W J U O I E D

Z D T K Q J O U S D H

# A Dose of Gross

| BACTERIA | FUNGUS | PHLEGM |
|----------|--------|--------|
| BILE | GERMS | PUS |
| BLACKHEAD | LICE | RASH |
| BOILS | MAGGOTS | SNOT |
| DANDRUFF | MOLD | WARTS |
| FART | MUCUS | ZITS |

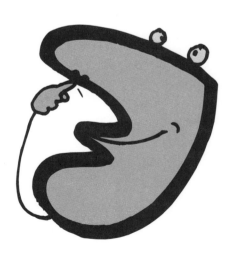

Wacky Word Games • Word Searches

| V | G | F | G | L | C | M | O | O | O | M | S | L | V | U |
|---|---|---|---|---|---|---|---|---|---|---|---|---|---|---|
| B | H | W | F | D | K | H | R | O | X | U | M | M | M | J |
| C | K | C | N | U | T | A | A | N | P | C | P | B | H | K |
| P | G | J | W | A | R | T | S | M | K | U | Y | O | P | F |
| P | V | C | R | X | I | D | H | D | I | S | L | I | C | E |
| C | H | E | S | P | Q | R | N | W | F | T | H | L | X | N |
| P | B | L | A | C | K | H | E | A | D | O | I | S | G | Q |
| O | O | I | E | X | Z | U | O | T | D | G | U | M | W | O |
| P | R | B | O | G | C | U | K | U | C | G | Q | R | K | F |
| N | Z | U | L | E | M | O | L | D | N | A | X | E | F | O |
| O | P | Q | F | H | F | B | X | U | P | M | B | G | O | O |
| B | V | S | E | J | V | W | F | V | B | S | T | I | Z |
| R | A | H | X | O | W | Z | A | V | N | V | Q | O |
| V | Y | V | D | O | Z | F | R | O | L | U | L |
| I | A | A | T | K | L | C | T | C | U | P |

SOLUTION FOUND ON PAGE 314.

225

# Do the Curley Shuffle

BACK IN A QUACK

CERTAINLY!

CURLY

GRRUUF

HELLO, HELLO,
HELLO

HEY FELLAS!

I'LL GET YOU!

I'LL MURDER YOU!

IMBECILE!

JOE

KNUCKLEHEAD!

LARRY

LOOK AT THE
GROUSE!

MOE

MORON!

NYUK!

POPSIE WOPSIE

QUIET!

SHEMP

WHAT'S THE BIG
IDEA?

WHY, I OUTTA!

WHY YOU!

WISE GUY!

WOOP! WOOP!

W O B B I L L G E T Y O U A X
H L R A U O Y Y H W U W A D J
A L J W C O D K P P O H Y A W
T E E I T K E U L T Y Y L E O
S H L S B A I Y S E R I N H O
T O I E D T S N S I E O I E P
H L C G Y T P F A U D U A L W
E L E U H H O U L Q R T T K O
B E B Y L E W U L S U T R C O
I H M L Y G E R E H M A E U P
G O I R R R I R F E L A C N N
I L O U R O S G Y M L Q O K
D L U C A U P J E P I R M
E E O M L S O A H I O J
A H P R F E P T T M P

Wacky Word Games • Word Searches

# EEK!

| | | |
|---|---|---|
| BEETLE | GOATEE | TWEEDLE DEE |
| BLEEP | JEEPERS | TWEETY |
| CREEPERS | PEE | WEE WEE |
| CREEPY | PEEK-A-BOO | WHEEDLE |
| EEL | SEEKER | YANKEE |
| GEEK | SHEEP | ZIP-A-DEE |

SOLUTION FOUND ON PAGE 315.

```
L  X  D  V  E  Z  M  R  R  I  A  G  N  V  T
B  R  M  G  D  I  N  T  Y  R  O  D  Z  G  R
J  Y  L  Z  D  D  H  S  Q  A  G  G  N  E  C
Z  A  L  A  C  G  S  E  T  X  S  P  C  R  E
I  P  X  H  L  R  R  E  H  Y  W  U  L  W  Z
G  S  U  T  P  E  E  K  A  B  O  O  W  C  U
L  T  M  B  W  W  P  E  K  L  E  M  R  G  M
Y  A  N  K  E  E  E  P  E  X  E  W  B  Q
C  N  Q  E  E  D  E  L  D  E  E  W  T  Z  X
F  L  W  H  A  J  J  T  L  P  R  G  G  L  T
M  X  S  P  D  V  P  D  Y  W  E  S  K  Q  E
R  U  I  H  E  E  E  X  D  O  N  H  P  S
Z  Z  A  S  M  E  T  T  E  T  S  I  V
S  H  P  R  H  V  D  D  K  D  L  V
S  R  X  W  H  E  M  H  D  B  M
```

Wacky Word Games • Word Searches

# Finding Who?

ANEMONE

BRUCE

DORY

"DARLA!"

"DUDE!"

"FISH ARE
FRIENDS"

GILL

"HEEERRRE'S
BRUCIE!"

LUCKY FIN

"MADE ME INK!"

MARLIN

MEMORY LOSS

"MINE! MINE!"

NEMO

"P. SHERMAN"

SHARK BAIT

SYDNEY

"VOILA! HE IS
CLEAN!"

```
N E E Q V Y S B J I Q C S I B
X I R A O N I P V S I B U X E
G C L L I G B O A S Z B D T Z
K U C R L K H S E O C O R E L
H R H A A O T L S L R U S I W
Y B K D H M N I F Y K C U L K
D S D N E I R F E R A H S I F
F E D C I M V E N O M E N A I
U R U P S E L N A M R E H S P
Z R D K C B M P Q E M A M Q G
B R E G L O A E H M C Q J J K
I E K Q E P S Y D N E Y Q O
G E X B A W R T X A N A C
E E P E N I M E N I M O
S H A R K B A I T D E
```

# Freaks of Nature

BEAKED SNAKE     FAIRY WREN     POLECAT

BEARDED DRAGON     FLYING FISH     POTBELLY PIG

COWBIRD     HAGFISH     SLIME HAG

CUCKOO     LOON     SLOTH BEAR

DODO BIRD     MOUSEBIRD     SUGAR GLIDERS

DWARF GOAT     NAKED MOLE RAT     WOODPECKER

```
U  N  S  J  S  F  I  C  U  C  K  O  O  A  C
H  U  O  C  X  W  O  O  D  P  E  C  K  E  R
F  T  A  O  G  F  R  A  W  D  G  X  K  K  F
T  A  C  E  L  O  P  P  K  R  E  A  E  S  A
D  R  I  B  E  S  U  O  M  I  N  Q  U  L  I
E  E  M  D  B  V  C  T  O  S  K  G  U  O  R
Z  L  J  R  W  B  D  B  D  T  A  O  B  T  Y
N  O  G  A  R  D  D  E  D  R  A  E  B  H  W
C  M  A  M  O  B  K  L  G  H  Z  E  Z  B  R
O  D  H  S  Z  A  A  L  H  L  Y  N  U  E  E
W  E  E  B  E  S  I  Y  B  T  W  U  V  A  N
B  K  M  B  I  D  D  P  E  Q  J  H  Z  R
I  A  I  P  E  D  R  I  B  O  D  O  D
R  N  L  R  U  H  A  G  F  I  S  H
D  H  S  I  F  G  N  I  Y  L  F
```

SOLUTION FOUND ON PAGE 316.

233

# Funny Phrases

*Search for the words listed in all CAPS.*

BEE in your bonnet?

CAT got your tongue?

CHICKEN scratch

Don't RAT on me!

FROG in your throat?

Get off your high HORSE!

I'll be a MONKEY'S uncle!

I'm in the DOGHOUSE!

I'm living in a FISHBOWL.

Let sleeping DOGS lie.

LOOK At what the cat dragged in!

The cat that swallowed the CANARY.

The cat's out of the BAG!

The FUR is going to fly!

When PIGS fly!

Your FLY is down!

You're a stool PIGEON!

You're BARKING up the wrong tree.

| | | | | | | | | | | | | | | |
|---|---|---|---|---|---|---|---|---|---|---|---|---|---|---|
| G | D | Z | Y | M | E | A | E | L | Y | Z | C | I | K | R |
| D | O | K | E | W | O | J | E | U | B | G | X | A | Y | J |
| K | T | H | C | C | I | R | F | R | N | L | A | R | E | E |
| C | E | H | M | W | T | H | C | Q | M | G | B | V | E | K |
| V | S | Y | K | K | P | F | L | Y | D | S | D | S | N | S |
| G | F | E | T | E | F | U | T | K | N | I | U | L | C | C |
| V | F | P | S | B | Q | R | Y | N | K | O | X | H | K | R |
| A | C | K | O | O | L | W | O | B | H | S | I | F | A | J |
| D | P | E | L | L | Y | E | H | G | E | C | A | T | J | D |
| F | N | Z | A | D | G | M | O | N | K | E | Y | S | Y | J |
| D | C | R | O | I | S | D | W | E | O | E | S | R | O | H |
| O | I | Q | P | P | X | G | N | I | K | R | A | B | B | |
| P | N | I | U | Z | D | W | O | G | D | N | B | O | | |
| Y | G | G | C | Y | H | B | A | D | A | Q | H | | | |
| S | X | V | X | P | B | H | B | C | N | B | | | | |

SOLUTION FOUND ON PAGE 316.



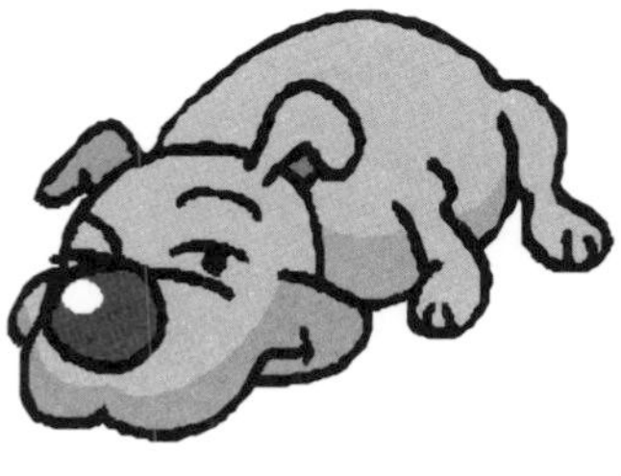

# Gatorade and Taffy

*Try reading each column out loud from top to bottom as fast as you can before you start your search. Now, do it again. And again. And again! Faster!*

| | | |
|---|---|---|
| GOOFY | GREEN GRASS. | TOADS |
| GEESE | THREE | TIPTOED |
| GLADLY | TWO-TOED | THROUGH |
| GULP | TAP DANCING | THE TERRIFIC |
| GATORADE® | TREE | TAFFY ON TUESDAY. |
| AND GRAZE | | |
| ON THE GLORIOUS | | |

**236**

```
D  O  W  R  Q  Q  A  T  S  G  X  C  T  T  D
X  Q  O  X  Z  P  L  D  U  F  S  I  A  F  X
X  V  Q  P  V  S  A  V  O  Z  Y  F  P  B  S
R  L  G  V  C  O  V  U  I  K  F  I  D  S  P
O  Z  Y  L  T  A  Z  O  R  Y  O  R  A  X  A
Z  J  C  R  I  T  N  T  O  C  O  R  N  R  F
P  C  E  W  P  X  H  N  L  T  G  E  C  Z  Z
O  E  Z  X  T  R  T  R  G  N  K  T  I  K  A
K  T  A  F  O  U  G  G  E  E  S  E  N  Q  R
Y  G  R  U  E  D  U  E  H  E  J  H  G  V  C
M  L  G  S  D  L  R  Z  T  W  O  T  O  E  D
U  H  D  R  P  G  X  H  N  W  M  Q  W  W
R  A  N  A  A  G  A  T  O  R  A  D  E
Y  I  A  L  L  Y  S  O  G  T  L  O
V  X  J  N  V  G  E  P  F  O  R
```

SOLUTION FOUND ON PAGE 317.

**237**

Wacky Word Games · Word Searches

# Giddish for Yiddish

BUBBIE (sweetie)

DUMKOPF (dummy)

FUTZ (to Fiddle Around)

GANIF (thief)

KHUTSPE (nerve)

KIBITZ (to meddle)

MASHUGGA (crazy)

MAYVEN (expert)

MAZEL (luck)

NEBISH (nerd)

NOSH (to snack)

OY! (disapproving sigh)

PUTZ (dummy)

SCHMATTAH (A rag)

SCHMOOZ (chatting)

SCHMUTZ (dirt)

SCHPEEL (pitch)

SHLEMAZEL (loser)

SHLEMIL (fool)

SHLEP (carry)

SHLOK (curse)

SHREK (monster)

SHTICK (routine)

TOOMEL (noise)

238

**239**

```
O  I  I  S  Z  X  V  N  O  Q  S  Q  R  I  Q
Z  D  S  C  H  M  A  T  T  A  H  J  I  K  V
L  S  C  H  P  E  E  L  B  D  L  L  X  Z  A
F  E  H  M  L  E  I  I  K  B  E  L  Z  K  N
G  Z  M  O  F  E  Z  Z  B  E  P  J  W  O  C
A  T  U  O  C  F  M  L  G  B  R  D  S  M  O
F  U  T  Z  O  G  G  A  G  G  U  H  S  A  M
W  P  Z  T  T  T  N  O  Z  M  L  B  S  Y  L
T  T  T  L  Z  I  U  P  K  E  M  C  K  V  J
F  U  I  S  F  A  B  O  M  P  L  C  C  E  C
V  V  X  R  P  C  P  I  H  S  I  B  E  N  R
M  K  J  A  I  F  L  E  K  T  K  V  F  T
L  W  R  X  Y  R  Z  T  H  U  L  A  C
H  N  K  K  O  L  H  S  H  H  T  J
F  I  C  C  M  G  B  M  J  K  R
```

# Go Berserk!

BALLISTIC

BATTY

BERSERK

BONKERS

CUCKOO

FLIP YOUR LID

FLIPPIN'

FRANTIC

FRUITY

HAYWIRE

ILLIN'

IN A TIZZY

KOOKY

OFF YOUR ROCKER

RAGIN'

SPAZZIN'

THROUGH THE ROOF

UNHINGED

Wacky Word Games · Word Searches

```
O  T  Z  K  F  E  G  P  V  W  E  C  S  C  H
U  F  O  O  R  E  H  T  H  G  U  O  R  H  T
D  G  F  E  R  C  H  S  D  O  F  S  B  D  S
A  L  R  Y  U  F  U  N  H  I  N  G  E  D  U
U  M  A  Q  O  B  A  L  L  I  S  T  I  C  O
Z  N  G  E  C  U  C  K  O  O  U  L  K  Z  I
F  I  I  V  R  S  R  I  S  M  R  K  K  K  Q
A  L  N  Z  I  I  Z  R  T  U  K  R  U  X  L
G  L  I  Y  Z  N  W  B  O  N  K  E  R  S  Z
O  I  C  P  L  A  A  Y  X  C  A  S  T  S  V
C  J  P  Y  P  T  P  W  A  K  K  R  G  D  G
T  J  G  C  T  I  Y  S  O  H  U  E  F  V
G  P  X  Y  L  Z  N  O  R  T  B  B  R
I  I  F  F  E  Z  K  S  F  T  N  R
F  R  U  I  T  Y  T  Y  Z  N  U
```

SOLUTION FOUND ON PAGE 318.

**241**

# Go Figure...

*Search for the words listed in all CAPS.*

What do you call a cat with a clock?
**PURRFECT TIMING**

What's a frog's favorite drink?
**CROAKA-COLA**

What do you call a lover of hot chocolate?
**COCOANUT**

What do you call a pig jumping into a fan?
**PORK CHOP**

What do you call a rabbit having a bad day?
**UNHOPPY**

What do you call a snake that bakes?
**PIE-THON**

What's a snake's favorite sport?
**SNAKEBOARDING**

What do you call a shark that throws snowballs?
**FROSTBITE**

What's a snowman's favorite cereal?
**FROSTED FLAKES**

What do you call a traveling turtle?
**TOUR-TOISE**

What do you call a tree with a hand?
**PALM TREE**

What's a tree's favorite drink?
**ROOT BEER**

What's a turtle's favorite type of aircraft?
**SHELLICOPTER**

What do you call a vacation for married rabbits?
**BUNNYMOON**

What do you call a vampire's dog?
**BLOODHOUND**

What's black, white and read all over?
**NEWSPAPER**

What do you call an operation for rabbits?
**HOPERATION**

What's the right time to see a dentist?
**TOOTH HURTY**

Wacky Word Games • Word Searches

```
C  R  E  T  P  O  C  I  L  L  E  H  S  G  R
G  J  Z  I  F  S  C  J  P  B  S  P  N  R  E
D  M  P  E  Y  E  R  E  A  E  Q  I  A  E  E
C  N  T  T  P  K  O  S  L  T  M  E  K  P  B
V  O  U  O  P  A  A  I  M  I  Q  T  E  A  T
K  O  N  O  O  L  K  O  T  B  X  H  B  P  O
P  M  A  T  H  F  A  T  R  T  X  O  O  S  O
O  Y  O  H  N  D  C  R  E  S  L  N  A  W  R
H  N  C  H  U  E  O  U  E  O  A  Z  R  E  H
C  N  O  U  F  T  L  O  Y  R  V  M  D  N  E
K  U  C  R  K  S  A  T  L  F  J  I  I  S  C
R  B  R  T  S  O  Z  O  T  B  L  N  N  K
O  U  Z  Y  X  R  Z  W  V  J  Z  U  G
P  T  Q  O  D  F  H  K  B  X  M  I
N  O  I  T  A  R  E  P  O  H  P
```

# Gotta Go, Gotta Go, Gotta Go!

DO YOUR BUSINESS

DO YOUR DOODIE

DOO DOO

GET BUSY

GO POOPIE

GO POTTY

GO TO THE BATHROOM

GOTTA GO

GOTTA SEE JOHNNY

LITTLE BOY'S ROOM

NUMBER ONE

NUMBER TWO

PEE PEE

TAKE A TINKLE

TINKIE WINKIE

TOILET

THE POWDER ROOM

WEE WEE

SOLUTION FOUND ON PAGE 319.

**245**

| | | | | | | | | | | | | | | |
|---|---|---|---|---|---|---|---|---|---|---|---|---|---|---|
| B | P | F | J | J | G | C | M | J | C | D | Q | U | Z | G |
| N | S | T | H | E | P | O | W | D | E | R | R | O | O | M |
| D | S | E | L | K | N | I | T | A | E | K | A | T | U | W |
| G | E | I | D | O | O | D | R | U | O | Y | O | D | N | E |
| Y | N | N | H | O | J | E | E | S | A | T | T | O | G | E |
| E | I | Q | I | R | F | J | T | O | H | D | N | X | E | W |
| E | S | E | I | K | N | I | W | E | I | K | N | I | T | E |
| P | U | Z | M | N | U | M | B | E | R | O | N | E | B | E |
| E | B | G | O | T | T | A | G | O | R | D | R | E | U | N |
| E | R | X | O | W | T | R | E | B | M | U | N | G | S | U |
| P | U | U | D | H | V | T | G | O | P | O | T | T | Y | Y |
| M | O | O | R | S | Y | O | B | E | L | T | T | I | L | |
| I | Y | O | T | O | I | L | E | T | R | L | Z | H | | |
| G | O | P | O | O | P | I | E | F | Q | T | Q | | | |
| M | D | O | O | D | O | O | D | N | H | O | | | | |

# Have You Ever Seen a...

BANANA SPLIT?

BOARD WALK?

BUTTER FLY?

CAR PET?

CAT FISH?

EAR RING?

EGG PLANT?

FISH BOWL?

HAIR SPRAY?

HORSE FLY?

ICE SCREAM?

NEEDLE POINT?

ROOT BEER FLOAT?

SODA POP?

TOE NAIL?

TOOTH BRUSH?

TUNA FISH?

TUNA MELT?

```
R  P  L  I  H  A  I  R  S  P  R  A  Y  D  Q
J  O  W  H  E  L  C  O  T  O  P  X  M  D  E
F  J  O  F  R  I  E  Z  W  P  K  F  B  W  E
J  A  B  T  B  A  S  Y  H  A  N  O  A  F  A
F  H  H  Z  B  N  C  Y  O  D  E  D  N  I  R
U  Z  S  S  O  E  R  L  R  O  E  O  A  F  R
E  Y  I  U  A  O  E  F  S  S  D  E  N  M  I
V  K  F  A  R  T  A  R  E  E  L  G  A  L  N
Z  V  H  Y  D  B  M  E  F  A  E  G  S  C  G
X  V  S  D  W  O  H  T  L  L  P  P  P  P  O
H  S  I  F  A  N  U  T  Y  F  O  L  L  N  C
I  A  F  W  L  R  S  U  O  X  I  A  I  K
R  Y  T  X  K  N  I  B  R  O  N  N  T
X  K  A  T  U  N  A  M  E  L  T  T
A  M  C  A  R  P  E  T  T  D  L
```

SOLUTION FOUND ON PAGE 319.

**247**

Wacky Word Games • Word Searches

# I Say, I Say, Boy!

ARRIBA!
(Speedy Gonzales)

CAN WE FIX IT?
(Bob the Builder)

DESPICABLE!
(Daffy Duck)

EXIT, STAGE LEFT!
(Snagglepuss)

HEY, BOO BOO!
(Yogi Bear)

HEY, ROCKY!
(Bullwinkle)

I YAM WHAT I YAM.
(Popeye)

JANE!
(George Jetson)

MEEP MEEP!
(Road Runner)

RUHROH!
(Scooby-Doo)

THAT'S ALL FOLKS!
(Porky Pig)

UH HUH, UH HUH
(Goofy)

VAMANOS!
(Dora the Explorer)

WASCALLY WABBIT!
(Elmer Fudd)

WHAT'S UP, DOC?
(Bugs Bunny)

WHOA MOMMA!
(Johnny Bravo)

YABBA DABBA DOO
(Fred Flintstone)

ZOINKS!
(Shaggy)

```
M  T  F  E  L  E  G  A  T  S  T  I  X  E  A
A  B  B  C  N  Z  O  I  N  K  S  N  E  W  R
Y  K  C  O  R  Y  E  H  B  L  E  V  G  M  T
I  W  H  A  T  S  U  P  D  O  C  J  E  S  K
T  N  R  O  Z  T  I  X  I  F  E  W  N  A  C
A  M  E  E  P  M  E  E  P  L  M  Y  A  W  R
H  E  Y  B  O  O  B  O  O  L  Q  X  B  H  U
W  A  S  C  A  L  L  Y  W  A  B  B  I  T  H
M  A  E  L  B  A  C  I  P  S  E  D  R  O  R
A  M  M  O  M  A  O  H  W  T  L  N  R  A  O
Y  O  O  D  A  B  B  A  D  A  B  B  A  Y  H
I  C  U  H  H  U  H  U  H  H  U  H  W  J
G  N  V  A  M  A  N  O  S  T  O  A  M
W  C  H  G  S  R  Y  Y  F  L  C  Q
E  Y  P  V  L  F  D  K  T  P  L
```

SOLUTION FOUND ON PAGE 320.

249

Wacky Word Games · Word Searches

# It's a Girl Thing

| | | |
|---|---|---|
| AMANDA BYNES | JESSICA SIMPSON | POWERPUFF GIRLS |
| ANGELICA | KIM POSSIBLE | RAVEN |
| BLUE | LILO | REN STEVENS |
| BRACEFACE | LINDSAY LOHAN | SABRINA |
| BRANDY | LIZZIE MCGUIRE | TAMERA |
| CADET KELLY | MOESHA | TIA |

250

```
Y  N  J  L  Y  L  L  E  K  T  E  D  A  C  S
A  R  E  M  A  T  E  T  B  K  R  D  B  L  L
D  G  S  V  M  B  L  F  R  O  I  L  R  C  E
R  D  S  H  A  J  B  G  A  N  U  I  E  B  H
B  O  I  R  N  R  I  M  C  E  G  N  N  M  M
R  P  C  P  D  G  S  Z  E  F  C  D  S  I  B
A  D  A  C  A  E  S  E  F  D  M  S  T  E  C
N  C  S  L  B  E  O  U  A  G  E  A  E  C  N
D  V  I  I  Y  O  P  A  C  T  I  Y  V  O  U
Y  U  M  L  N  R  M  N  E  T  Z  L  E  T  N
H  T  P  O  E  J  I  I  V  K  Z  O  N  P  I
V  I  S  W  S  G  K  R  K  V  I  H  S  L
C  V  O  R  I  F  N  B  L  T  L  A  S
C  P  N  L  A  W  B  A  M  Z  J  N
D  E  V  F  K  A  H  S  E  O  M
```

# It's Hip To Be Square(Pants)

"AROUND TOWN!"

BIKINI BOTTOM

GARY

"HEY, SANDY!"

"I'M READY!"

"JELLYULICIOUS!"

KRABBY PATTIES

KRUSTY KRAB

"MEOW."

MR. KRABS

"OH, BARNACLES!"

"OH, TARTAR SAUCE."

"OHHHHHH, POOP."

PATRICK

PINEAPPLE HOUSE

"SKIDDLY-DIDDLY-DO!"

"SOAP, WHAT IS SOAP?"

SQUIDWARD

| O | S | G | R | Q | N | J | A | E | B | M | E | O | W | H |
| D | H | G | A | R | Y | E | K | S | J | X | K | H | Q | L |
| Y | B | W | B | T | D | L | R | U | Y | C | O | T | N | Y |
| L | J | O | I | B | A | L | A | O | D | X | H | A | W | F |
| D | A | H | K | A | E | Y | B | H | N | S | H | R | O | Z |
| D | K | B | I | R | R | U | B | E | A | Q | H | T | T | O |
| I | H | A | N | K | M | L | Y | L | S | U | H | A | D | N |
| D | G | R | I | Y | I | I | P | P | Y | I | H | R | N | D |
| Y | P | N | B | T | G | C | A | P | E | D | H | S | U | O |
| L | P | A | O | S | S | I | T | A | H | W | P | A | O | S |
| D | K | C | T | U | W | O | T | E | B | A | O | U | R | B |
| D | J | L | T | R | V | U | I | N | K | R | O | C | A | |
| I | R | E | O | K | I | S | E | I | M | D | P | E | | |
| K | Y | S | M | P | S | C | S | P | J | M | E | | | |
| S | B | A | R | K | R | M | K | P | Q | L | | | | |

SOLUTION FOUND ON PAGE 321.

253

Wacky Word Games · Word Searches

# It's Raining Cats and Dogs

CAT IN THE HAT

FELIX

GARFIELD

HEATHCLIFF

MORRIS

PINK PANTHER

SYLVESTER

TIGGER

TOP CAT

ASTRO

BENJI

BLUE

GOOFY

LASSIE

ODIE

PLUTO

SCOOBY-DOO

SNOOPY

```
N C F X H K Z O U R U I T S M
J T A C P O T Q T J X V O M C
Z Y C T N B P S I I U U O D X
G A R F I E L D X B G R P Z S
S O F Z A N U U F H R G Z H S
P Y L E Q J T C E I E N E U O
U B K U Y I O H S L H A M R W
Z W J H S Y L V E S T E R D J
Z B W O A B P K C H N U M A J
M O O D Y B O O C S A S T R O
K X E I S S A L K X P T Y X S
M H Y E Q P I D B B K K Z H
U Z G O O F Y P O O N S S
A M D N F B X F E L I X
K L N A Y B Y U O Z P
```

SOLUTION FOUND ON PAGE 321.

**255**

# It's Your Yucky Day!

BACK HAIR

BELLY BUTTON LINT

CLAMMY PALMS

CRUSTY BOOGERS

DRAGON BREATH

EARWAX

EYE SNOT

FESTERING ZITS

GREASY HAIR

MUCK MOUTH

NAIL FUNGUS

PRICKLY SCABS

RUNNY NOSE

SMELLY FEET

STINKY PITS

TOE JAM

TONGUE FUR

YELLOW TEETH

```
Y  J  O  E  S  T  I  P  Y  K  N  I  T  S  N
D  R  A  G  O  N  B  R  E  A  T  H  Q  O  R
B  E  F  N  A  I  L  F  U  N  G  U  S  Z  I
A  Y  W  S  M  L  A  P  Y  M  M  A  L  C  A
C  E  M  D  C  N  M  U  C  K  M  O  U  T  H
K  S  R  E  G  O  O  B  Y  T  S  U  R  C  Y
H  N  F  E  S  T  E  R  I  N  G  Z  I  T  S
A  O  Z  T  F  T  O  E  J  A  M  D  C  W  A
I  T  L  B  R  U  F  E  U  G  N  O  T  T  E
R  P  R  O  F  B  E  S  O  N  Y  N  N  U  R
S  M  E  L  L  Y  F  E  E  T  Q  R  I  X  G
P  R  I  C  K  L  Y  S  C  A  B  S  Z  W
E  J  Y  E  L  L  O  W  T  E  E  T  H
X  A  W  R  A  E  Z  R  T  H  H  P
M  B  Z  Q  V  B  U  Y  D  P  T
```

# Knock, Knock...

*Search for the words listed in all CAPS.*

## Who'sThere?

**ATLAS.** Atlas who?
Atlas, I'm here!

**BARBIE.** Barbie who?
Barbie Q!

**BOO.** Boo who?
Don't cry, it's just
a joke.

**CATCH.** Catch who?
Bless you.
Need a tissue?

**DISHES.** Dishes who?
Dishes the police,
open up!

**DWAYNE.** Dwayne who?
Dwayne the bathtub,
I'm dwowning!

**JOE.** Joe who?
Joe mama!

**JUSTIN.** Justin who?
Justin time!

**LITTLE OLD LADY.** Little
old lady who?
I didn't know you could
yodel.

**MAJOR.** Major who?
Major look!

**NUNYA.** Nunya who?
Nunya business.

**OLIVE.** Olive who?
Olive you!

**ORANGE.** Orange who?
Orange you glad
to see me?

**PEA.** Pea who?
Pea you!

**SEVEN.** Seven who?
Seven ate nine.

**THERESA.** Theresa who?
Theresa green!

**WHO.** Who who?
What are you, an owl?

**YAH!** Yah who?
Yahoo! Let's party!

Q Y Z R P I R I N K P X I Z H
J V E P L S S W L A F M B L S
P X I E G O K A O E O H I I E
M P A R L Z E O L W L T H K N
Z B V Z J S B L I V T O C I I
D U P J M Y U W V L O P T V H
R O T O A Z T H E R E S A Q L
E F A N J T R O Q I U Q C D C
J E G U O N L R H J B S F E O
M Q Q N R D W A Y N E R N Y V
O U W Y L I L N S R P E A X W
O S F A A S G G X K O P Y B
U O D J K H N E V E S I Y
T Y N G F E L U O C F V
G J V T N S U J D R T

# Lame Names

ADAM SAPPLE

ANITA BATH

BOB FRAPPLES

CARRIE OAKEY

CHRIS P. NUGGET

DENNIS TOFFICE

EARL E. BIRD

FRANK N. STEIN

GLADYS EEYA

HUGO FIRST

IDA WHANA

JED I. KNIGHT

JUSTIN CASE

KENNY DEWITT

LEO TARRED

MAY O'NAYS

NICK L. ANDIME

SHERI COLA

```
I  A  Y  E  E  S  Y  D  A  L  G  R  U  J  S
P  C  D  N  I  C  K  L  A  N  D  I  M  E  Y
M  K  H  A  I  L  E  O  T  A  R  R  E  D  A
Y  S  E  R  M  E  A  N  A  H  W  A  D  I  N
D  E  N  N  I  S  T  O  F  F  I  C  E  K  O
R  L  K  S  N  S  A  S  W  W  E  F  R  N  Y
I  P  H  A  H  Y  P  P  N  L  P  M  Y  I  A
B  P  T  U  O  E  D  N  P  K  F  P  V  G  M
E  A  A  C  G  E  R  E  U  L  N  Q  T  H  T
L  R  B  F  D  O  I  I  W  G  E  A  B  T  H
R  F  A  T  W  S  F  R  C  I  G  E  R  Z  R
A  B  T  M  O  S  F  I  R  O  T  E  W  F
E  O  I  L  E  F  S  R  R  A  L  T  T
S  B  N  V  H  M  R  U  M  S  C  A
E  S  A  C  N  I  T  S  U  J  T
```

SOLUTION FOUND ON PAGE 323.

261

# LoL

BBL (be back later)

BFN (bye for now)

BION (believe it or not)

BRB (be right back)

BTDTGTTS
(been there done that
got the t-shirt)

BTW (by the way)

CYA (see ya)

GA (go ahead)

GTG (got to go)

JK (just kidding)

LOL (laughing
out loud)

LTNS (long time no see)

MYOB (mind your
own business)

OMG (oh my gosh)

QT (cutie)

ROFL (rolling on
floor laughing)

TTFN (tah tah
for now)

WTG (way to go)

| | | | | | | | | | | | | | | |
|---|---|---|---|---|---|---|---|---|---|---|---|---|---|---|
| L | N | Q | G | H | L | W | W | G | D | Y | G | M | G | J |
| W | B | T | D | T | G | T | T | S | N | V | Z | A | I | Q |
| S | I | B | Z | R | G | C | Z | D | N | F | T | T | Y | H |
| B | O | Y | M | G | R | R | I | M | W | T | B | R | B | C |
| U | N | M | J | X | H | U | G | K | H | W | L | G | P | Y |
| N | J | P | Q | N | X | V | R | I | H | O | T | F | L | K |
| V | H | L | C | G | V | S | R | Q | L | P | B | Q | O | K |
| P | V | C | B | D | B | I | G | H | J | S | A | M | X | R |
| E | O | U | E | H | G | L | M | A | J | H | G | I | R | B |
| S | Z | Z | H | J | K | N | P | N | G | B | S | X | E | T |
| F | E | Q | G | N | V | J | B | M | J | H | P | Y | L | P |
| Q | K | N | Z | C | S | J | M | X | P | Q | D | R | O | |
| U | P | V | K | Z | K | E | K | M | C | H | Y | P | | |
| J | W | M | S | Y | F | Y | N | R | R | S | U | | | |
| R | C | G | F | H | A | N | X | Z | V | E | | | | |

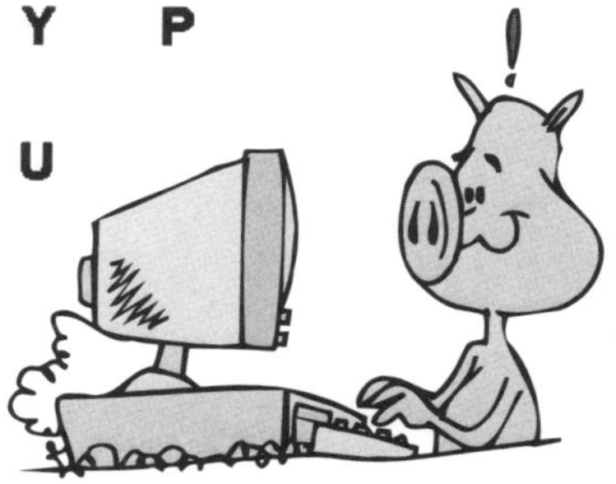

SOLUTION FOUND ON PAGE 323.

# London Calling

ARSE (bottom)

BANGERS (sausage)

BLOODY (extremely)

BLOWER (telephone)

BOBBY (policeman)

BOOT (car trunk)

BUGGAR (rascal)

CHEERIO (goodbye)

DICKY (sick)

DIGGS (lodging)

DODGY (shady)

FLOG (sell)

GANDER (glance)

GOB (mouth)

HOOTER (nose)

JOLLY (very)

KIP (nap)

MIND THE GAP (watch your step)

NAFF (uncool)

PARKY (CHILLY)

QUID (pound note)

RUCK (fight)

WANKER (idiot)

WHIRLY (dizzy)

```
V  H  V  T  R  E  I  E  K  N  B  P  B  V  I
L  R  V  R  C  R  L  R  S  C  A  O  L  I  Q
Z  F  A  K  D  J  T  M  B  R  L  A  B  J  E
D  L  C  K  V  O  I  X  I  C  A  L  P  B  T
M  U  E  G  O  L  F  X  C  B  O  G  A  S  Y
B  A  W  B  Y  L  R  I  H  W  G  N  G  S  X
Z  E  E  G  A  Y  I  L  E  Z  G  G  E  U  R
W  M  J  R  U  C  K  R  E  E  I  R  H  P  B
W  J  F  F  H  T  E  C  R  D  E  K  T  T  G
E  K  A  M  H  K  U  S  I  T  H  Y  D  A  B
K  I  P  N  N  B  L  O  O  D  Y  G  N  F  Z
W  Q  O  A  T  A  S  O  I  T  S  D  I  L
Z  V  W  F  R  Z  H  U  A  G  E  O  M
X  L  P  F  C  K  Q  J  C  R  S  D
U  B  L  W  F  Z  Y  Q  T  Z  W
```

SOLUTION FOUND ON PAGE 324.

265

Wacky Word Games • Word Searches

# Looney Library

Search for the words listed in all CAPS.

## Book Title

1. *Attack of the Lion*
2. *Clean Up Your Yard*
3. *Danger!*
4. *Don't Hurt Me!*
5. *Downpour!*
6. *Tacky Clothes*
7. *Falling Trees*
8. *History of Texas*
9. *Hours in the Bathroom*
10. *I Don't Get It*
11. *I Love Crowds*
12. *Longest River in the US*
13. *Old Furniture*
14. *Remodeling Your House*
15. *Snakes of the World*
16. *The Broken Bed*
17. *The Color of Eggs*
18. *The Fall of a Watermelon*

## Written By

1. CLAUDIA ARMOFF
2. RAY CLEAVES
3. LUKE OUT
4. I. BRUCE EASLEY
5. WAYNE DWOPS
6. POLLY ESTER
7. TIM BURR
8. AL E. MOE
9. R.U. DUNNYETT
10. ANITA CLEW
11. MORRIS MERRIER
12. MRS. HIPPIE
13. ANNE TEAK
14. BILL JEROME HOME
15. ANNA CONDA
16. SQUEAK E. SPRINGS
17. SUMMER BROWN
18. S. PLATT

Wacky Word Games • Word Searches

```
W  P  I  B  R  U  C  E  E  A  S  L  E  Y  Q
Q  V  C  P  O  L  L  Y  E  S  T  E  R  R  N
S  H  S  T  Q  L  A  N  M  G  O  X  G  U  Q
U  R  S  R  U  S  U  A  O  N  V  H  Q  D  A
M  R  E  Y  V  P  D  N  R  I  L  L  K  U  N
M  U  V  X  I  O  I  N  R  R  M  U  A  N  N
E  B  A  W  S  W  A  A  I  P  R  K  L  N  E
R  M  E  E  U  D  A  C  S  S  S  E  E  Y  T
B  I  L  L  J  E  R  O  M  E  H  O  M  E  E
R  T  C  C  P  N  M  N  E  K  I  U  O  T  A
O  C  Y  A  Z  Y  O  D  R  A  P  T  E  T  K
W  K  A  T  J  A  F  A  R  E  P  Q  D  G
N  D  R  I  Z  W  F  K  I  U  I  F  I
T  B  V  N  D  X  T  S  E  Q  E  J
S  P  L  A  T  T  U  J  R  S  B
```

SOLUTION FOUND ON PAGE 324.

**267**

# Lose Your Lunch

BARF

BLOW CHOW

BLOW CHUNKS

GAG

HACK

HEAVE

HURL

ILL

LOSE YOUR LUNCH

PAVEMENT PIZZA

PUKE

PURGE

RALPH

SPEW

TOSS YOUR COOKIES

UPCHUCK

VOMIT

YACK

```
H  I  A  K  Q  P  G  P  X  B  A  C  F  E  K
F  C  P  X  P  Y  M  G  Z  L  E  A  W  G  L
A  K  N  P  Z  R  A  M  N  O  R  K  S  R  B
X  K  D  U  D  B  E  C  P  W  J  H  U  U  Y
I  V  F  S  L  B  B  J  K  C  U  H  C  P  U
Z  Z  H  R  V  R  A  L  P  H  A  C  K  H  L
T  O  S  S  Y  O  U  R  C  O  O  K  I  E  S
X  I  N  G  G  C  F  O  F  W  O  O  L  A  U
G  B  S  V  P  K  T  O  Y  O  A  P  L  V  L
A  Z  Z  I  P  T  N  E  M  E  V  A  P  E  B
G  A  O  N  W  T  T  W  E  P  S  B  V  O  F
O  F  G  Z  S  K  N  U  H  C  W  O  L  B
Q  I  V  Z  H  F  E  C  V  Z  M  G  L
Z  L  L  W  F  C  N  K  K  I  P  Q
Z  Y  D  F  A  F  Z  J  T  R  G
```

SOLUTION FOUND ON PAGE 325.

269

# Muppet Mumbo Jumbo

ABSOTIVELY

BORK! BORK! BORK!

CAMILLA!

CAN YOU DIG IT?

EAT DRUMS!

ELECTRIC MAYHEM

HEEEY-YA!

HI-HO!

KERMIT DE FROG

KERMY!

LIKE, FER SURE!

LOUDER!

MEEP-MEEP!

MOI?

MUPPET NEWS FLASH!

PIGGY!

PIGS IN SPAAAACE!

POSOLUTELY

THE MUPPET SHOW!

TRUST ME!

WANT WOMAN!

WHAT A TRIP!

WOCKA-WOCKA!

YAAAY!

M W O H S T E P P U M E H T K
E R C H A K C O W A K C O W Q
H S A L F S W E N T E P P U M
Y Y N H E E E Y Y A I I B K W
A L Y G G I P M T R G O E E A
M E O H I H R D T S R R R B W
C T U L F E R A I K M U S A M
I U D M K U T N B I S O N E E
R L I O M A S O T R T T E M A
T O G S H P R D E I W P T L R
C S I W A K E F V O M S L E Y
E O T A B F E E M E U I D A
L P A O R K L A E R M U A
E C R O I Y N P T A O A
E K G L R N U G C L Y

SOLUTION FOUND ON PAGE 325.

271

Wacky Word Games · Word Searches

# My Name is...

ADAM MEWAY

ANITA BERGER

BARB DWYER

CHAD TERBOCKS

CHESTER DRAWERS

ELLA VADOR

HARMON IKKA

HUGH DEMANN

IDA HOE

IMA HOGG

IRA FUZE

IVANA TINKEL

JIM SHORTS

JOE KING

KENT COOK

LOU STOOTH

PETER PANZ

STU PITT

```
C  Y  N  F  H  A  R  M  O  N  I  K  K  A  G
D  H  N  E  L  L  A  V  A  D  O  R  N  D  Q
S  Y  A  W  E  M  M  A  D  A  V  I  V  Y  Q
W  L  M  D  P  A  L  O  U  S  T  O  O  T  H  H
C  H  E  S  T  E  R  D  R  A  W  E  R  S  A
S  G  D  K  Q  E  T  W  B  I  A  Y  Y  R  Y
T  G  H  Q  N  T  R  E  Y  W  D  B  R  A  B
R  P  G  J  N  I  R  B  R  H  M  A  T  Q  J
O  J  U  T  Y  G  T  I  O  P  W  Z  H  O  U
H  O  H  D  E  I  M  A  X  C  A  D  H  O  B
S  E  D  R  Z  A  O  I  N  X  K  N  F  A  E
M  K  K  S  H  I  F  J  S  A  N  S  Z  E
I  I  K  O  O  C  T  N  E  K  V  L  M
J  N  G  B  T  E  Z  U  F  A  R  I
S  G  S  T  U  P  I  T  T  P  J
```

SOLUTION FOUND ON PAGE 326.

**273**

Wacky Word Games · Word Searches

# Not Dealing with a Full Deck

BANANAS

BATS IN BELLFRY

BONKERS

BRAINSICK

COOKED

CRACKPOT

DEMENTED

DETACHED

DINGBAT

FRUIT LOOP

FRUITCAKE

HALFBAKED

KOOK

LOONEY TOON

LOST YOUR
MARBLES

LUNATIC

NOT WRAPPED
RIGHT

NUTCASE

PSYCHO

SCHIZO

SCREWBALL

TOUCHED

UNHINGED

WACK JOB

274

| | | | | | | | | | | | | | | |
|---|---|---|---|---|---|---|---|---|---|---|---|---|---|---|
| T | O | L | S | I | K | Q | T | A | B | G | N | I | D | U |
| H | C | O | E | K | A | C | T | I | U | R | F | E | F | L |
| G | O | H | L | U | N | A | T | I | C | Y | M | H | B | L |
| I | O | C | B | A | N | A | N | A | S | E | K | G | R | A |
| R | K | Y | R | F | L | L | E | B | N | I | S | T | A | B |
| D | E | S | A | F | R | U | I | T | L | O | O | P | I | W |
| E | D | P | M | D | C | E | E | O | V | W | K | W | N | E |
| P | E | D | R | O | Z | D | O | P | U | S | T | A | S | R |
| P | C | E | U | I | U | N | Z | K | N | R | N | C | I | C |
| A | A | H | O | D | E | T | A | C | H | E | D | K | C | S |
| R | A | C | Y | Y | S | S | G | A | I | K | Q | J | K | V |
| W | N | U | T | C | A | S | E | R | N | N | P | O | A | |
| T | R | O | S | K | O | O | K | C | G | O | L | B | | |
| O | O | T | O | Z | I | H | C | S | E | B | U | | | |
| N | H | A | L | F | B | A | K | E | D | D | | | | |

SOLUTION FOUND ON PAGE 326.

**275**

Wacky Word Games • Word Searches

# Oops! I Did It Again!

| | | |
|---|---|---|
| BABOON | GOOBER | PHOOEY |
| BOOHOO | GOOEY | STOOGE |
| BUFFOON | GOOFY | TOOT |
| DOODAD | GOOGLE | VAVOOM |
| DOOZY | HOOLIGAN | WHOOPEE |
| GADZOOKS | NINCOMPOOP | YAHOO |

276

```
V  G  P  B  B  P  V  J  F  N  Q  G  W  F  B
S  X  S  K  O  O  Z  D  A  G  F  H  F  Y  J
L  B  U  F  F  O  O  N  H  T  R  Y  A  J  W
J  W  Y  E  O  O  H  P  L  D  F  H  O  C  N
X  V  U  E  D  B  Y  O  M  O  O  V  A  N
R  R  S  A  L  E  E  P  O  O  H  W  H  G  A
K  A  D  T  R  G  O  G  L  Z  C  K  B  X  G
Y  C  K  O  O  A  O  I  S  Y  D  N  X  V  R
M  D  Z  O  D  B  G  O  O  B  E  R  I  L  G
N  N  T  T  S  A  E  J  G  F  Y  B  H  N  X
V  S  U  K  N  B  B  C  S  R  L  X  D  F  J
Y  D  D  B  T  O  H  H  G  T  I  C  I  V
Y  P  D  S  N  O  T  K  N  P  R  X  D
X  U  R  R  I  N  H  Z  Z  Z  U  X
K  Z  H  L  N  J  O  T  I  H  X
```

SOLUTION FOUND ON PAGE 327.

**277**

# A Romp in the Swamp

"A GIRL DRAGON!"

"A NOBLE STEED"

DONKEY

DULOC

FAR FAR AWAY

FIONA

"GO AWAY, DONKEY!"

"GOT A TIC-TAC®?"

"I AM PUSS IN BOOTS."

"I'M A REAL BOY!"

"I'M AN OGRE!"

"I'M MAKING WAFFLES!"

LORD FARQUAAD

"NOT MY BUTTONS!"

"OGRES HAVE LAYERS."

SHREK

THE SWAMP

"YOU'RE A MONSTER!"

O G R E S H A V E L A Y E R S
N L Q N A N O B L E S T E E D
N D A A U Q R A F D R O L U J
O I Y A W A R A F R A F F O E
T K B M T F J R K C F I O N A
M E R E T S N O M A E R U O Y
Y R V H U P M A W S E H T K M
B H I M A N O G R E E O C N T
U S T O O B N I S S U P M A I
T S N A G I R L D R A G O N A
T L I W K G O T A T I C T A C
O G O A W A Y D O N K E Y O
N I M A R E A L B O Y K L
S M S B E Y M N A V E U
I K B W E I M P I U D

SOLUTION FOUND ON PAGE 327.

**279**

# Sally, Cherie, Socks and Sheep

*Try reading each column out loud from top to bottom as fast as you can before you start your search. Now, do it again. And again. And again! Faster!*

| | | |
|---|---|---|
| CHERIE'S | SOLELY ON | SHILLY-SHALLIED |
| SHOP | SATURDAYS | SEVEN |
| STOCKS | IN SUMMER. | SHAVEN |
| SHORT | SILLY | SHEEP |
| SPOTTED | SALLY | SOUTH |
| SOCKS | SWIFTLY | IN SEPTEMBER. |

280

```
N  M  U  S  N  S  O  C  K  S  P  N  I  L  K
W  O  Y  H  E  W  H  U  H  I  N  B  P  A  I
W  U  Y  I  H  I  B  O  E  L  J  B  J  X  O
O  B  T  L  N  F  R  N  P  L  H  V  B  S  F
X  G  S  L  E  T  U  E  X  Y  S  Q  S  Y  H
Z  H  E  Y  V  L  K  V  H  R  H  C  O  W  K
G  R  D  S  A  Y  O  E  K  C  G  M  I  W  O
B  S  T  H  H  D  X  S  A  R  A  C  Q  Q  T
Y  L  L  A  S  B  R  E  M  M  U  S  N  I  N
J  I  I  L  O  H  T  U  O  S  P  J  T  L  C
Q  R  C  L  J  E  E  S  T  O  C  K  S  C  Y
A  N  Y  I  W  J  M  E  T  A  O  H  C  C
J  P  R  E  B  M  E  T  P  E  S  N  I
C  A  K  D  F  H  E  W  I  N  B  U
A  R  G  X  X  D  K  Z  X  A  Q
```

SOLUTION FOUND ON PAGE 328.

**281**

# Schmoopie Whoopie

| | | |
|---|---|---|
| BOO BEAR | KITTEN | PUMPKIN |
| BOO-BOO | LOVE BUCKET | SCHNOOKUMS |
| BUBSY | LOVEFACE | SNUGGLES |
| CUDDLE MUFFIN | LOVEY | STUD MUFFIN |
| CUPCAKE | MR. MAN | SUGAR DUMPLIN' |
| FOO-FOO | POOKIE | SWEET PEA |
| HONEY BUNNY | POOPSIE | SWEETIE PIE |
| HUNZIE AND ZUNZIE | PUDDIN' POP | SWEETUMS |

282

| O | B | V | F | S | R | W | Z | P | O | O | K | I | E | Z |
|---|---|---|---|---|---|---|---|---|---|---|---|---|---|---|
| N | I | K | P | M | U | P | Z | N | E | T | T | I | K | T |
| E | I | P | E | I | T | E | E | W | S | M | R | M | A | N |
| R | W | F | D | S | W | E | E | T | P | E | A | T | C | G |
| A | R | M | F | J | S | N | U | G | G | L | E | S | P | P |
| E | I | Z | N | U | Z | D | N | A | E | I | Z | N | U | H |
| B | N | I | L | P | M | U | D | R | A | G | U | S | C | B |
| O | O | E | W | U | T | E | K | C | U | B | E | V | O | L |
| O | O | O | F | O | O | F | L | O | V | E | F | A | C | E |
| B | Q | F | B | G | P | U | D | D | I | N | P | O | P | K |
| E | I | S | P | O | O | P | K | Z | D | Y | S | B | U | B |
| N | U | R | J | H | O | N | E | Y | B | U | N | N | Y | |
| Y | L | U | S | M | U | K | O | O | N | H | C | S | | |
| H | S | M | U | T | E | E | W | S | K | Q | L | | | |
| Y | E | V | O | L | X | A | A | G | M | S | | | | |

Wacky Word Games • Word Searches

# Starving Students

BEEFARONI®

CAMPBELL'S®

CEREAL

CHEEZ WHIZ®

DINTY MOORE®

DOMINO'S

DORITOS®

FISH STICKS

FRIES

HOSTESS®

HOT POCKETS®

HUNGRY-MAN®

LEAN CUISINE®

LEGGO MY EGGO®

MAC AND CHEESE

MICRO POPCORN

NACHOS

POP TARTS®

RAGU®

RAMEN NOODLES

SLIM JIM®

SPAGHETTIOS®

SPAM®

TATER TOTS®

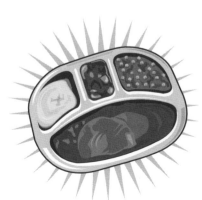

Wacky Word Games · Word Searches

```
I  F  S  T  Z  I  H  W  Z  E  E  H  C  O  N
N  L  L  A  Y  S  T  N  M  E  S  E  G  S  A
O  E  I  T  Y  O  P  R  R  Z  E  G  Z  T  C
R  A  M  E  N  N  O  O  D  L  E  S  L  R  H
A  N  J  R  C  I  O  C  H  Y  H  K  H  A  O
F  C  I  T  Y  M  M  P  M  O  C  C  O  T  S
E  U  M  O  Y  O  A  O  T  S  D  I  S  P  R
E  I  T  T  A  D  G  P  I  L  N  T  T  O  A
B  S  N  S  F  G  O  O  S  L  A  S  E  P  G
I  I  Q  R  E  C  S  R  K  E  C  H  S  H  U
D  N  I  L  K  R  G  C  Q  B  A  S  S  R  P
C  E  R  E  A  L  B  I  Y  P  M  I  P  O
S  O  T  I  R  O  D  M  V  M  A  F  C
K  S  O  I  T  T  E  H  G  A  P  S
N  A  M  Y  R  G  N  U  H  C  D
```

SOLUTION FOUND ON PAGE 329.

# Stupid Pet Names

BUFFY

BUTTERCUP

BUTTONS

CONFETTI

COUNTESS

CREAMPUFF

CUDDLES

FLUFFY

HUGSY

KISSES

MISS PRISS

MR. TINKLES

MR.WIGGLESWORT

MRS. TIGGIEWIGGIE

POOCHIE

SMOOCHIE

SNUGGLES

TWINKLE TOES

E K H W Y S E L D D U C M C L
I I F Z F Y M U K B H L R H W
G U H W V V X O U H G C T D W
G T R C W C U T O K Q R I K Z
I C W C O V T A R C O Q N N R
W V R I O O R E J W H M K A D
E X O E N N P D S R N I L F V
I S R S A K F E K I S S E S E
G I E T B M L E O S S S S B M
G Y B L G G P E T E V P M H H
I N Q U G Y B U T T E R C U P
T S B I F G K N F O I I G W
S G W Y F F U L F F E S Z
R R L D Q O Y N V K Y S
M G Z O C E P O S Z C

SOLUTION FOUND ON PAGE 329.

**287**

# Things That Make You Go Hmmm...

*Search for these fun oxymorons!*

ALL ALONE     JUNK FOOD     STUDENT TEACHER

BAD LUCK     NEAR MISS     TERRIBLY NICE

EVEN ODDS     PLASTIC GLASSES     TOP FLOOR

FREEZER BURN     PRETTY UGLY     WALL STREET

FRONT END     SECOND BEST     WHITE GOLD

JUMBO SHRIMP     STILL MOVING     WICKED GOOD

**288**

Wacky Word Games • Word Searches

```
G  N  I  V  O  M  L  L  I  T  S  F  Y  B  P
X  Z  B  D  N  E  T  N  O  R  F  U  W  C  M
X  F  N  R  U  B  R  E  Z  E  E  R  F  O  P
P  S  S  I  M  R  A  E  N  H  D  W  B  X  S
M  G  D  O  O  G  D  E  K  C  I  W  I  P  D
I  K  E  N  O  L  A  L  L  A  O  Q  R  E  D
R  W  A  L  L  S  T  R  E  E  T  E  H  A  O
H  S  R  O  O  L  F  P  O  T  T  Z  A  F  N
S  E  S  S  A  L  G  C  I  T  S  A  L  P  E
O  T  E  R  R  I  B  L  Y  N  I  C  E  G  V
B  D  O  O  F  K  N  U  J  E  Y  Y  E  D  E
M  W  H  I  T  E  G  O  L  D  A  D  I  U
U  P  B  A  D  L  U  C  K  U  Y  Q  S
J  P  H  F  Y  H  K  B  R  T  B  R
W  S  E  C  O  N  D  B  E  S  T
```

Wacky Word Games • Word Searches

# TomFoolery

| | | |
|---|---|---|
| BUFFOONERY | HOOPLA | MOCKERY |
| CAPER | HORSEPLAY | MONKEYSHINE |
| DIDO | HULLABALOO | MUMMERY |
| DROLLERY | HUMOR | ROMP |
| ESCAPADE | JOKE | SHENANIGAN |
| FROLIC | LAMPOONERY | SKYLARK |
| HIGH JINKS | LARK | SPREE |
| HOODWINK | MERRIMENT | TRICKERY |

290

Wacky Word Games · Word Searches

```
V  C  Y  L  F  N  R  O  H  O  D  N  Q  Y  G
N  Z  R  Y  K  Y  X  L  J  K  W  N  U  R  S
M  E  E  R  P  S  H  A  R  E  U  A  K  E  T
F  Y  M  E  R  R  I  M  E  N  T  G  N  K  F
A  K  M  K  K  F  G  P  P  I  M  I  I  C  T
T  H  U  C  C  O  H  O  A  B  H  N  W  I  P
Y  L  M  O  I  C  J  O  C  S  O  A  D  R  I
S  E  P  M  L  H  I  N  Y  J  R  N  O  T  A
B  U  F  F  O  O  N  E  R  Y  S  E  O  Q  S
H  U  M  O  R  J  K  R  G  B  E  H  H  K  V
I  Q  P  O  F  N  S  Y  J  R  P  S  Y  J  Y
C  L  F  P  O  O  L  A  B  A  L  L  U  H
A  E  N  M  M  E  S  C  A  P  A  D  E
O  D  I  D  R  O  L  L  E  R  Y  I
Y  P  X  T  J  M  R  A  K  B  V
```

SOLUTION FOUND ON PAGE 330.

**291**

Wacky Word Games • Word Searches

# Too Pooped to Pop!

| | | |
|---|---|---|
| BEAT | DONE | POOPED |
| BURNED OUT | DRAINED | SHOT |
| BUSHED | FINISHED | SPENT |
| CONKED | GONE | TOAST |
| COOKED | KNACKERED | TORQUED OUT |
| CRASHED | LAST LEG | WIPED |
| DEAD | LIMP | WORN |
| DOG'S BARKING | OVER | ZONKED |

```
T  X  B  P  L  R  U  S  C  Z  E  A  G  K  U
I  S  E  L  C  G  H  T  S  Z  G  D  S  L  J
Q  D  A  O  E  O  G  E  V  O  E  T  I  A  O
X  W  T  O  T  N  N  O  H  N  Q  M  P  S  X
Y  D  I  B  T  E  I  K  I  K  P  B  O  T  Q
Q  Y  K  P  N  J  K  A  E  E  A  U  O  L  Z
M  R  R  O  E  I  R  P  D  D  Z  R  P  E  D
E  M  D  N  P  D  A  V  E  Y  Q  N  E  G  B
R  D  E  H  S  U  B  H  R  U  A  E  D  V  U
Z  R  K  C  R  A  S  H  E  D  I  D  L  Y  O
S  Y  O  T  C  I  G  D  K  X  L  O  U  F  I
P  W  O  R  N  L  O  E  C  O  M  U  S  X
X  M  C  I  K  U  D  E  A  D  I  T  U
K  D  F  H  T  K  J  Y  N  B  I  L
X  N  W  I  F  J  T  G  K  D  S
```

SOLUTION FOUND ON PAGE 331.

**293**

# Tush Talk

| | | |
|---|---|---|
| APPLE BOTTOM | CAN | KEISTER |
| BACKSIDE | CHEEKS | MOON |
| BOOTY | CULO | ONION |
| BUM | DERRIERE | REAR |
| BUNS | FANNY | RUMP |
| BUTT | GLUTEUS MAXIMUS | SEAT |
| BUTTOCKS | GOT BACK | TAIL |
| CABOOSE | HEINIE | TUSH |

| | | | | | | | | | | | | | | |
|---|---|---|---|---|---|---|---|---|---|---|---|---|---|---|
| F | Q | Y | C | A | U | T | D | V | W | W | N | P | G | E |
| V | M | H | T | D | E | U | L | I | Q | Z | Q | L | J | X |
| F | U | G | R | E | T | S | I | E | K | G | U | H | Z | Z |
| R | L | E | F | R | C | H | O | O | B | T | I | T | C | P |
| U | R | E | A | R | E | Q | K | O | E | O | I | A | U | R |
| M | O | O | N | I | O | N | M | U | B | P | O | A | L | J |
| P | V | E | N | E | D | I | S | K | C | A | B | T | O | G |
| F | H | I | Y | R | Z | M | B | R | A | S | C | I | Y | R |
| S | E | Y | T | E | A | U | S | U | L | R | K | K | M | T |
| C | K | Z | P | X | T | E | N | D | P | D | A | L | C | L |
| Z | W | O | I | T | A | S | U | D | M | R | W | I | N | T |
| J | C | M | O | T | T | O | B | E | L | P | P | A | K | |
| Z | U | C | Z | Y | H | O | X | E | R | E | C | T | | |
| S | K | E | E | H | C | W | K | B | V | C | L | | | |
| S | J | R | F | D | U | H | K | N | X | X | | | | |

SOLUTION FOUND ON PAGE 331.



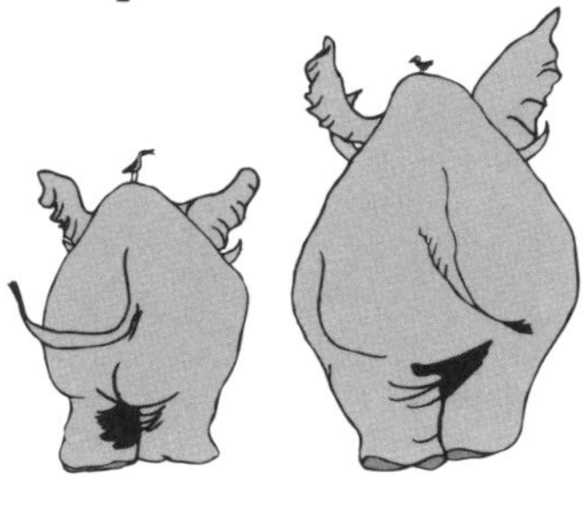

# Under the Weather

BARF

BLOW CHOW

BLOW CHUNKS

EXPEL

GAG

HACK

HEAVE

HURL

ILL

KECK

LOSE YOUR LUNCH

PAVEMENT PIZZA

PUKE

PURGE

RALPH

SEASICK

SOUR

SPEW

THROW UP

TOSS COOKIES

UP CHUCK

VOMIT

WRETCH

YACK

Q U U Y H O L M Q K B G G A G
B L O W C H O W I L S Y Z M T
H S G W N T A S O S E Z Q I Q
S B P R U F P W W U I P U U T
A R A U L R C V T P K K X I O
P U W O R H T R T C O I H E X
J M H S U G H N I H O G P Y H
K F P N O Y E S M U C B L E N
C B K X Y M A F O C S I A W Y
F S B M E E V C V K S H R R C
C C N V S P E W K F O E D Z F
G C A N O U I E G I T F G V
U P I L L K E C K C A H D
Q U A L U T X I H U R L
H R N G P K L M I H P

SOLUTION FOUND ON PAGE 332.

**297**

Wacky Word Games · Word Searches

# Wacky Word Play

*Search for the words listed in all CAPS.*

**COOKOUT**
A cook's day off

**DETAIL**
Removing a tail

**DOUGHNUT**
Holey food

**FEATHERBRAINED**
Fuzzy-headed

**GHOST TOWN**
A town with
haunted houses

**HATCHET**
What hens do to eggs

**HEROES**
What a guy does
in a boat

**HIGH SCHOOL**
A classroom on
the top floor

**ILLEGAL**
A sick bird

**LITTLE DIPPER**
A small boy swimming

**MISTLETOE**
When you're missing
a toe

**MOTHBALL**
A dance for moths

**QUARTERBACK**
$.25 in change

**RELIEF**
What trees
do in spring

**REMIND**
A brain transplant

**WILDLIFE**
Having fun!

**WOODCHUCK**
Throwing wood

**WORKOUT**
An outside job

SOLUTION FOUND ON PAGE 332.

**299**

```
J  T  U  V  L  E  T  U  N  H  G  U  O  D  D
G  G  X  R  O  T  U  O  K  R  O  W  E  G  C
H  T  F  E  O  F  O  T  Q  V  M  N  H  S  V
D  C  Q  P  H  Y  K  D  U  H  I  O  E  L  Y
N  S  S  P  C  U  O  U  A  A  S  F  R  W  P
I  W  G  I  S  A  O  X  R  T  T  L  O  U  T
M  I  I  D  H  T  C  B  T  C  L  L  E  X  F
E  L  L  E  G  C  R  O  E  H  E  A  S  F  A
R  D  L  L  I  E  W  B  R  E  T  B  H  N  I
E  L  E  T  H  N  O  I  B  T  O  H  X  I  D
L  I  G  T  Q  Q  B  X  A  D  E  T  A  I  L
I  F  A  I  K  C  U  H  C  D  O  O  W  Q
E  E  L  L  L  K  Y  H  K  O  W  M  C
F  G  N  S  W  X  E  Z  O  P  V  C
S  T  H  T  Y  R  B  W  Z  E  Q
```

# We Love Lucy!

BABALU

C'MON, ETHEL!

DESILU

DISHWATER
BLONDE

DON'T YOU DARE!

ETHEL

FROWSY REDHEAD

GIMBLES

GOBLOOTS

I HAVE A PLAN!

ISN'T THAT A
DILLY?

LITTLE RICKY

LUCY, I'M HOME!

MCGILLICUDDY

NOW, FRED!

NOW, LUUUCY!

RICARDO

RICKY

RIDICULOUS!

SPLAININ' TO DO!

THE MERTZES

TROPICANA

VITAMEATAVEGAMIN

WAH!

300

```
N  X  L  R  S  T  H  E  M  E  R  T  Z  E  S
I  Y  Y  D  D  U  C  I  L  L  I  G  C  M  N
M  L  W  G  I  M  B  L  E  S  M  S  Z  O  Y
A  L  U  L  I  S  E  D  Y  P  H  G  R  H  P
G  I  I  H  A  V  E  A  P  L  A  N  K  M  O
E  D  N  O  L  B  R  E  T  A  W  H  S  I  D
V  A  O  T  I  R  A  H  L  I  D  B  T  Y  R
A  T  W  R  T  I  D  D  E  N  E  A  O  C  A
T  A  L  O  T  D  U  E  H  I  R  B  O  U  C
A  H  U  P  L  I  O  R  T  N  F  A  L  L  I
E  T  U  I  E  C  Y  Y  E  T  W  L  B  W  R
M  T  U  C  R  U  T  S  N  O  O  U  O  R
A  N  C  A  I  L  N  W  O  D  N  A  G
T  S  Y  N  C  O  O  O  M  O  L  C
I  I  D  A  K  U  D  R  C  K  R
V  K  K  E  Y  S  Q  F  R  N
```

SOLUTION FOUND ON PAGE 333.

**301**

Wacky Word Games • Word Searches

# What Do You Call a...

*Search for the words listed in all CAPS.*

Centipede crossed
with a parrot?
**WALKIE TALKIE**

Clock being thrown
out the window?
**TIME FLIES**

Country in a rush?
**RUSSIA**

Couple of kids
in a tree?
**PAIR**

Dinosaur playing golf?
**TEE REX**

Dog with no legs?
**STAY**

Guy in a frame
on the wall?
**ART**

Movie rated "Arrrgh!"?
**PIRATE MOVIE**

Twins hanging
on a window?
**CURT AND ROD**

Person who runs
at top speed?
**MAX**

Sad baby chick?
**BLUEBIRD**

Skeleton who won't
cross the road?
**NO GUTS**

Teddy bear
after dinner?
**STUFFED**

Two women
on your roof?
**EVES**

What a bee drives?
**BEE-M-W**

Thing that starts, ends
and is filled with T?
**TEAPOT**

302

```
K V G I A N Q U D Y Z A F O X
K T I N K Q P H Y D A C U M S
D Y O Z K F X E R E E T F X M
T E C P S U S I Q E P H S N S
P V F T A H B K N I A H P I Q
B S F F A E D L R L I K R K E
K E A C U R T A N D R O D Q Z
J I O L B T T T B I U U Y D R
Z L B H G E S E V L S X J C J
U F M A M N E I U G S A M L S
F E E O O M V K V M I O I Y F
O M V G W Q E L I C A V P L
K I U G H F C A V H Z X Y
E T Y W N Q S W L C Q B
S B R F D T K U S J P
```

# Whatchamacallit?

CONTRAPTION        FLUMADIDDLE        THINGAMAJIG

DOODAD             GIMMICK            THINGY

DOOFUNNY           GIZMO              WHAT'S-ITS-NAME

DOOHICKEY          RIGAMAJIG          WHOSEE-WHATSEE

DOOJIGGER          THINGAMABOB        WHOSIT

FANDANGLE          THINGAMADOODLE     WIDGET

| | | | | | | | | | | | | | | |
|---|---|---|---|---|---|---|---|---|---|---|---|---|---|---|
| N | Y | I | E | T | H | I | N | G | Y | I | W | O | C | Y |
| F | F | S | L | H | I | O | Q | D | Z | G | Y | O | N | E |
| E | L | D | D | I | D | A | M | U | L | F | N | N | E | K |
| G | G | L | O | N | W | H | O | S | I | T | U | S | S | C |
| I | I | T | O | G | H | P | D | E | R | F | T | H | V | I |
| J | J | E | D | A | A | B | C | A | O | A | S | T | N | H |
| A | A | N | A | M | T | V | P | O | H | K | W | D | R | O |
| M | M | C | M | A | S | T | D | W | T | C | G | O | L | O |
| A | A | B | A | B | I | R | E | G | G | I | J | O | O | D |
| G | G | Q | G | O | T | E | G | I | Z | M | O | D | O | U |
| N | I | F | N | B | S | J | I | A | Q | M | H | A | I | Q |
| I | R | P | I | O | N | T | E | G | D | I | W | D | U | |
| H | P | B | H | F | A | N | D | A | N | G | L | E | | |
| T | J | W | T | K | M | X | C | D | M | H | W | | | |
| G | X | Z | X | W | E | D | J | K | M | L | | | | |



SOLUTION FOUND ON PAGE 334.

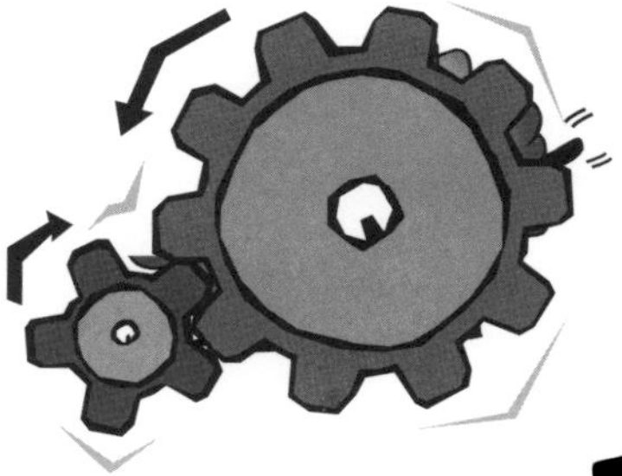

# What's in a Name?

*Search for the words listed in all CAPS.*

## What do you name a . . .

Woman in your dishwater?
DAWN

Woman in your garden?
LILY

Man hanging on a wall?
ART

Man hit by lightning?
ROD

Man holding a chain?
LINK

Man sitting on your doorstep?
MATT

Man on a BBQ grill?
FRANK

Man on a golf course?
CHIP

Man on a stage?
MIKE

Man sitting on a hill?
CLIFF

Man throwing up?
CHUCK

Man trapped in a bottle?
POP

Man water-skiing?
SKIP

Man who floats?
BOB

Man praying?
NEIL

Woman in a vase?
ROSE

Woman in a hole?
PEG

Woman lying on a beach?
SANDY

**306**

| | | | | | | | | | | | | | | |
|---|---|---|---|---|---|---|---|---|---|---|---|---|---|---|
| C | M | Z | V | B | W | Y | D | E | W | J | D | I | R | H |
| P | N | I | D | T | A | P | S | M | Y | K | I | W | D | B |
| T | L | X | F | T | D | O | K | D | A | W | N | H | D | P |
| A | H | X | A | F | R | A | N | K | O | T | N | H | T | E |
| T | T | R | L | B | I | A | I | Q | F | R | T | U | G | O |
| J | T | C | O | S | S | L | L | D | Z | E | A | S | N | Y |
| E | Q | Z | O | O | T | I | C | H | U | C | K | C | B | N |
| B | C | Y | A | A | E | L | Y | C | H | I | S | I | H | H |
| G | O | V | S | N | L | Y | C | I | P | B | G | X | M | Y |
| D | W | F | H | P | P | K | P | E | G | O | I | E | J | Q |
| P | J | J | L | P | G | N | X | I | T | B | P | Y | Z | K |
| D | Y | B | X | U | J | L | C | J | X | V | C | P | A | |
| A | P | M | H | W | E | X | J | W | F | U | I | V | | |
| H | N | I | S | J | T | K | N | J | Z | S | Z | | | |
| W | U | K | B | C | G | E | O | H | T | X | | | | |

SOLUTION FOUND ON PAGE 334.

307

Wacky Word Games • Word Searches

# What's the 411?

*Search for the words listed in all CAPS.*

**BLING BLING**
(jewelry)

**BOO**
(girlfriend or boyfriend)

**BOUNCE**
(gotta go)

**CHILL**
(relax)

**CRIB**
(your home)

**DISS**
(disrespect)

**FLOSSIN'**
(showing off)

**GIVE PROPS**
(say thanks)

**HOMEY**
(friend)

**ICE**
(diamonds)

**ILL**
(wrong)

**PHAT**
(cool)

**RIDE**
(car/transportation)

**SHORTY**
(girlfriend)

**SWEET**
(great)

**UNITS** (parents)

**WASSUP?**
(What's up?)

**YO!**
(Hi/Hey!)

```
Y  J  W  S  O  N  W  C  V  K  Y  E  D  X  P
V  B  I  T  E  E  W  S  J  L  E  E  B  U  M
H  W  O  D  K  R  C  A  I  J  W  P  B  O  O
U  F  I  K  C  G  N  I  S  S  O  L  F  J  J
D  R  M  A  I  S  J  I  S  S  I  D  Y  L  B
P  W  H  G  D  N  S  T  I  N  U  T  T  I  F
Q  P  K  K  R  Q  R  G  N  T  P  R  U  T
E  B  X  B  Z  L  M  B  S  M  Q  U  O  A  U
B  U  O  O  F  L  L  F  I  S  M  F  H  Q  O
Y  M  T  U  G  I  V  E  P  R  O  P  S  H  V
C  D  A  P  N  H  O  M  E  Y  C  F  K  E  F
Z  G  C  G  R  C  G  G  R  V  J  J  D  C
Q  Y  X  S  Q  A  E  W  H  J  P  X  K
W  W  V  O  Q  C  W  Q  K  X  P  F
X  U  M  Q  D  Y  B  W  D  J  J
```

SOLUTION FOUND ON PAGE 335.

★ 309

# When Good Food Goes Bad

BITTER JUICE

BRUISED BANANAS

BURNT TOAST

CHUNKY GRAVY

CURDLED MILK

FLAT SODA

GREEN CHEESE

LIMP LETTUCE

MOLDY MAYO

MUSHY MELON

RANCID MEAT

ROTTEN EGGS

SOGGY CEREAL

SOUPY ICE CREAM

SOUR GRAPES

STALE CRACKERS

STINKY TUNA

YESTERDAY'S SUSHI

**311**

```
I  M  A  E  R  C  E  C  I  Y  P  U  O  S  U
C  S  A  N  A  N  A  B  D  E  S  I  U  R  B
H  T  C  G  L  P  H  I  G  S  N  S  I  S  M
U  A  U  R  A  J  T  T  Y  T  O  E  A  T  O
N  L  R  E  E  C  U  T  T  E  L  P  M  I  L
K  E  D  E  R  R  T  E  S  R  E  A  A  N  D
Y  C  L  N  E  O  A  R  A  D  M  R  D  K  Y
G  R  E  C  C  T  E  J  O  A  Y  G  O  Y  M
R  A  D  H  Y  T  M  U  T  Y  H  R  S  T  A
A  C  M  E  G  E  D  I  T  S  S  U  T  U  Y
V  K  I  E  G  N  I  C  N  S  U  O  A  N  O
Y  E  L  S  O  E  C  E  R  U  M  S  L  A
Y  R  K  E  S  G  N  O  U  S  V  S  F
P  S  Y  J  G  G  A  C  B  H  M  J
Y  V  U  F  P  S  R  L  S  I  I
```

# Solutions

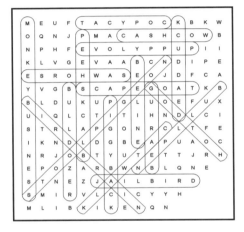

**ANIMAL TALK—PAGE 216**

**312**

**BOYS WILL BE BOYS—PAGE 218**

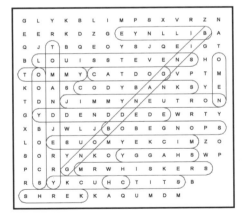

# Solutions

## BUST A MOVE!—PAGE 220

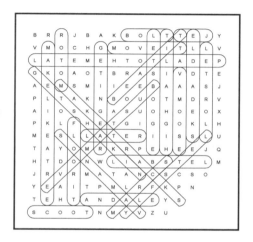

## BUTTER, BUGS & BEARS—PAGE 222

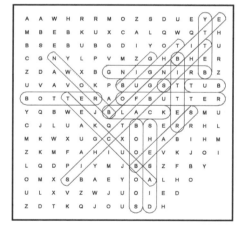

# Solutions

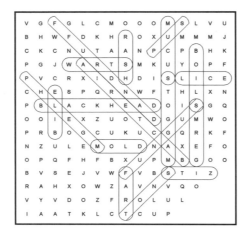

**A DOSE OF GROSS—PAGE 224**

**DO THE CURLEY SHUFFLE—PAGE 226**

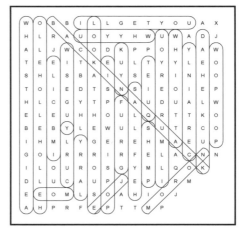

# Solutions

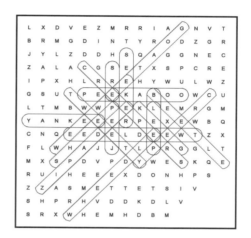

**EEK!—PAGE 228**

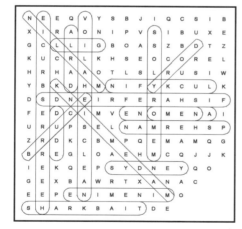

**FINDING WHO?—PAGE 230**

315

# Solutions

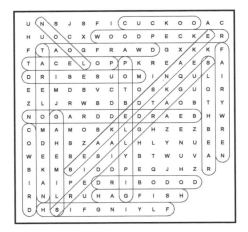

**FREAKS OF NATURE—PAGE 232**

**FUNNY PHRASES—PAGE 234**

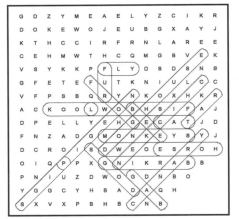

# Solutions

**GATORADE AND TAFFY—PAGE 236**

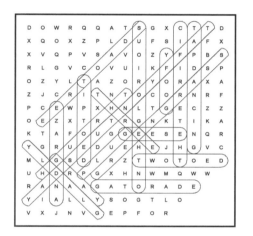

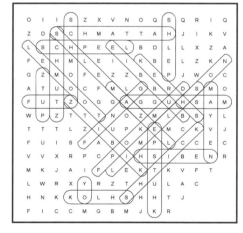

**GIDDISH FOR YIDDISH—PAGE 238**

# Solutions

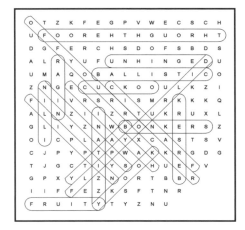

**GO BERSERK!—PAGE 240**

**GO FIGURE . . . —PAGE 242**

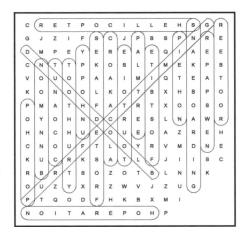

318

# Solutions

GOTTA GO, GOTTA GO,
GOTTA GO!—PAGE 244

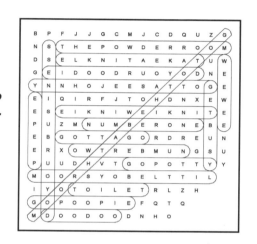

HAVE YOU EVER SEEN A . . .—PAGE 246

# Solutions

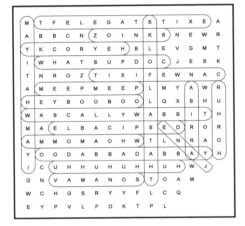

**I SAY, I SAY, BOY!—PAGE 248**

**320**

**IT'S A GIRL THING—PAGE 250**

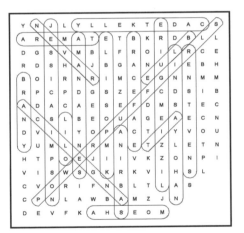

# Solutions

**IT'S HIP TO BE SQUARE(PANTS)—PAGE 252**

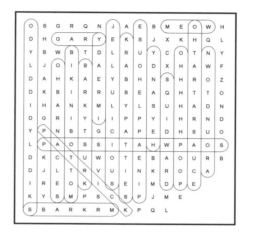

**IT'S RAINING CATS AND DOGS—PAGE 254**

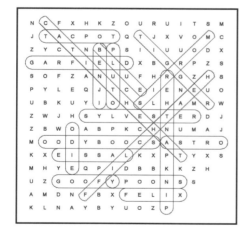

# Solutions

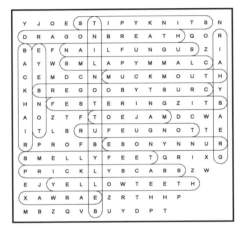

**IT'S YOUR YUCKY DAY!—PAGE 256**

**KNOCK, KNOCK . . . —PAGE 258**

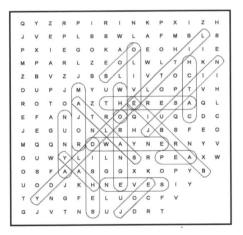

# Solutions

**LAME NAMES—PAGE 260**

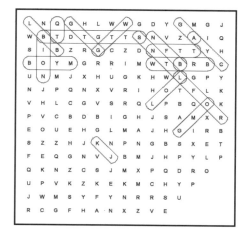

**LOL—PAGE 262**

# Solutions

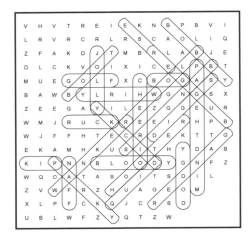

**LONDON CALLING—PAGE 264**

**324**

**LOONEY LIBRARY—PAGE 266**

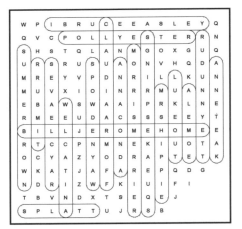

# Solutions

**LOSE YOUR LUNCH—PAGE 268**

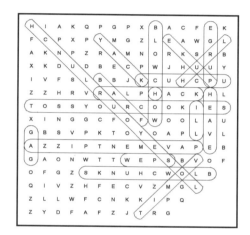

**MUPPET MUMBO JUMBO—PAGE 270**

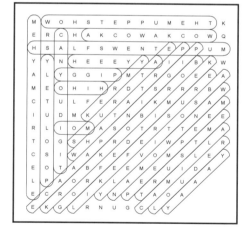

Wacky Word Games · Word Searches

# Solutions

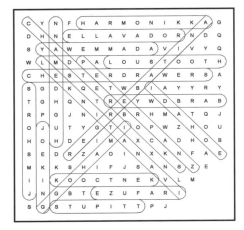

MY NAME IS . . . —PAGE 272

**326**

NOT DEALING WITH A
FULL DECK—PAGE 274

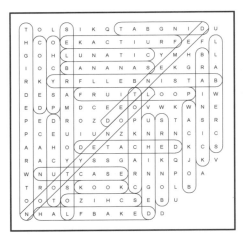

# Solutions

**OOPS! I DID IT AGAIN!—PAGE 276**

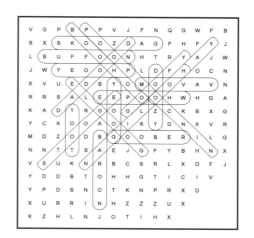

**A ROMP IN THE SWAMP—PAGE 278**

# Solutions

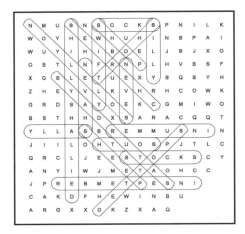

**SALLY, CHERIE, SOCKS AND SHEEP—PAGE 280**

328

**SCHMOOPIE WHOOPIE—PAGE 282**

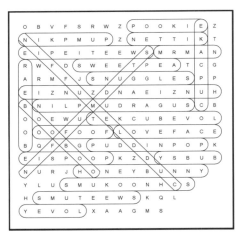

# Solutions

**STARVING STUDENTS—PAGE 284**

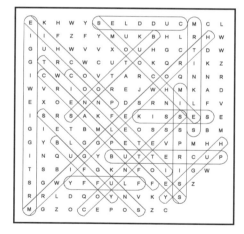

**STUPID PET NAMES—PAGE 286**

# Solutions

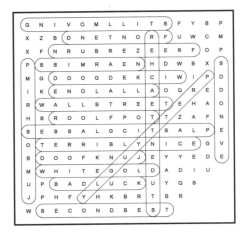

**THINGS THAT MAKE YOU GO HMMM . . . —PAGE 288**

**TOMFOOLERY—PAGE 290**

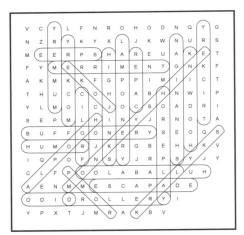

330

# Solutions

**TOO POOPED TO POP!—PAGE 292**

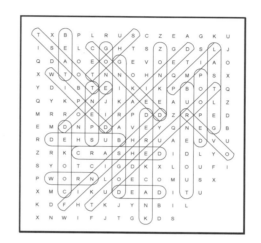

331

**TUSH TALK—PAGE 294**

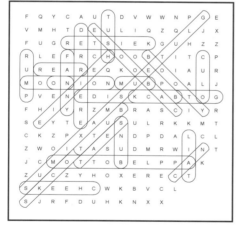

# Solutions

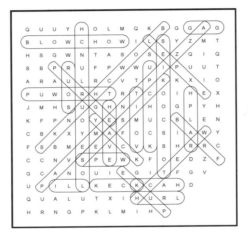

## UNDER THE WEATHER—PAGE 296

## WACKY WORD PLAY—PAGE 298

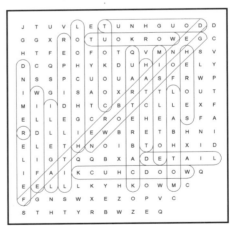

# Solutions

WE LOVE LUCY!—PAGE 300

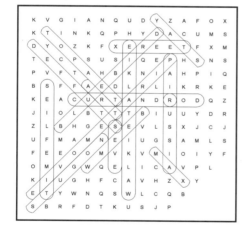

WHAT DO YOU CALL A . . .—PAGE 302

# Solutions

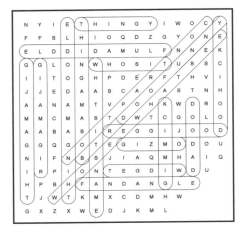

**WHATCHAMACALLIT?—PAGE 304**

**334**

**WHAT'S IN A NAME?—PAGE 306**

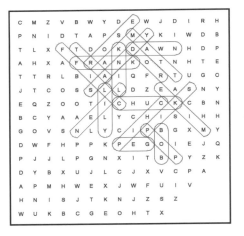

# Solutions

**WHAT'S THE 411?—PAGE 308**

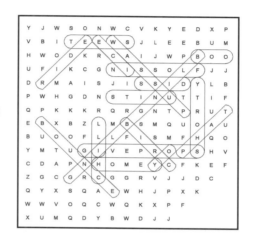

**WHEN GOOD FOOD GOES BAD—PAGE 310**

# About the Authors

### RIDDLES

ERIN ANTHONY lives with her family in Southern Illinois. She wants you to know that no animals were harmed in the writing of this book. She tested these riddles only on her son, whose groans in the laboratory seemed like a very good sign.

### BRAINTEASERS

BOB MOOG co-founded University Games in 1985 and has been creating games, brainteasers, word puzzles and the like since childhood. He is the author of several other books, including *Gummy Bear Goes to Camp*, *20 Questions®*, *30 Second Mysteries®* and *Batty Brainteasers*.

### WORD MUD

MARIA LLULL is a longtime creator and solver of word puzzles. She first honed her puzzling and gaming skills as a University Games staff member and now combines her successful career as a freelance writer with daily chess matches against her 10-year-old son Zack.

### WORD SEARCHES

CHERIE MARTORANA ZAMBERNARDI first started inventing games as a child to entertain her family. Later she headed for San Francisco where she honed her craft working for University Games. Today, Cherie creates, develops and plays games for a living (and for fun!) back home on Boston's North Shore.